GEOLOGISTS' ASSOC

GEOLOGY OF THE MANCHESTER AREA

Second Edition

by R. M. C. EAGAR and F. M. BROADHURST

With contributions by:-

A. E. Adams

R. S. W. Braithwaite

R. H. Johnson

K. Riley

P. Selden

I. M. Simpson

D. B. Thompson

Edited by J. T. Greensmith

Notes. *The details of routes given in these guides do not imply a right of way. The onus on obtaining permission to use footpaths and to examine exposures rests with the user of the Guide, who should carefully observe the Code for Geological Field Work issued from the Librarian, The Geologists' Association, c/o Department of Geological Sciences, University College London, Gower Street, London WC1E 6BT.*

In particular, those in charge of parties should ensure that there is no indiscriminate hammering of, or collecting from, exposures and that no damage is caused to property.

Any information (e.g. change in footpaths, filling-in of quarries, threat to SSI's, new exposures) that would update and improve a revised edition of this Guide would be welcomed by the Association.

CONTENTS

List of Figures

✦ ✦ ✦ ✦

List of Tables

PREFACE

R. M. C. Eagar and F. M. Broadhurst

This revised edition of the Manchester Guide covers the same area (Figure 1) as its predecessor (Broadhurst, *et al.*, 1970), but we have included more excursions and have also attempted to provide a wider range of geological interests in the itineraries chosen. The rocks exposed range in age from the Dinantian (Lower Carboniferous) to the Triassic and include superficial coverings of Pleistocene and Recent sediments. Of the sixteen itineraries described two are devoted to the Dinantian, five to the Silesian, covering parts of the Namurian (formerly Millstone Grit) and the Westphalian (Coal Measures), four to the Triassic, and three to the Pleistocene and Recent. The last two itineraries are concerned respectively with mineralisation and mining and with the building stones of Manchester.

More references to reading have also been included in this guide. Part of this increase is the inevitable result of increased knowledge and especially of the publication of syntheses of geological facts and theory directly or indirectly relating to the Manchester area. However, some chapters include short sections summarising topics such as local mineralisation, the history of mining in the district and some local industrial history, for instance in Itineraries IX and XV; and somewhat increased lists of references are provided in these instances, a few to specialist literature. These chapters provide a new element in this guide which we hope will prove useful to readers who may wish to follow up their particular interests. Localities have been numbered serially within each itinerary.

We are much indebted to landowners and others concerned with granting permission to enter private property and particular locations within property of the National Trust. Where permission must be sought by individuals or parties, names with addresses and telephone numbers are given in the itineraries concerned. It is strongly advisable to apply well in advance of the proposed visit.

Over much of the country described the user of this guide is requested scrupulously to refrain from using a hammer. There are a few places where active weathering of large exposures does not preclude hammering. For instance, in moorland areas where clayrocks are being eroded, a little hammer work can yield nicely preserved fossils without fear of depletion of the site. Such sections have been indicated by the authors concerned. There are also places, such as waste tips and mine dumps, where a keen eye can still discover rewarding specimens, notably of minerals (e.g. in Itinerary XV).

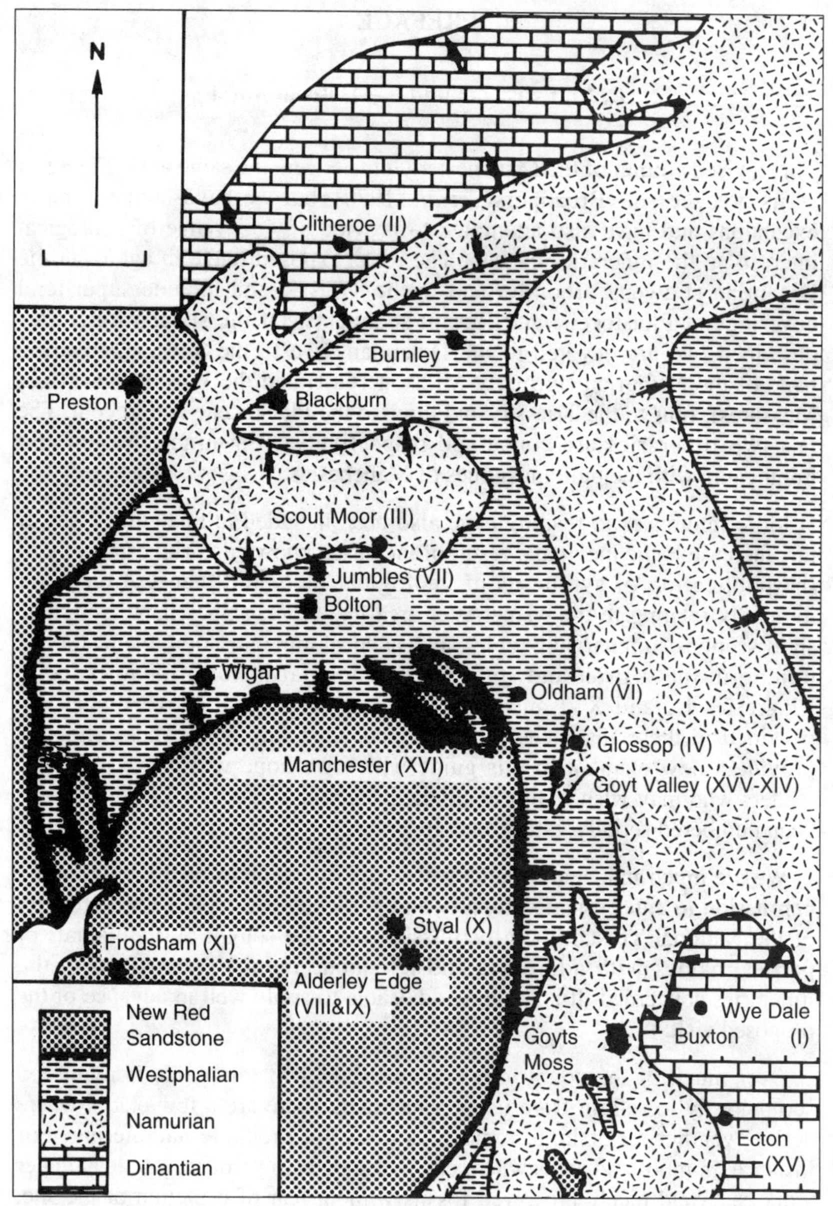

Figure 1. Simplified geological map of the Manchester area showing the general structure and the itineraries described. Arrows show the general direction of dip of strata. Heavy lines indicate some major faults. The scale bar is equal to 8 km.

We are grateful to Miss Patricia Crook for typing and to Mr. Richard Harley for preparing all the diagrams. The authors of the building stones excursion are grateful for the help and advice received in particular from Messrs. G. S. Bagot (of Leach, Rhodes and Walker), A. A. Bruce (of John Fyfe plc), D. G. S. Jesper (of D. G. S. Jesper Ltd.), A. Kumar (of Madon Industries Ltd.), and A. Wilson (of Bernard Thorpe and Partners).

Figures 1, 4 to 7, 10, 11, 14 and 15 are reproduced by permission of the Director, British Geological Survey (Crown copyright reserved).

GEOLOGY OF THE MANCHESTER AREA

R. M. C. Eagar and F. M. Broadhurst

The Manchester area, as part of the north and northwest Midlands of England (Figure 1), was initially moulded by numerous major events, many of which we have begun to unravel only in the last twenty-five years. By the late 1950's we knew that changes in past climates, for instance the slow transformation of tropical swamps, the source of Manchester's coal, to an arid area of moving sand dunes, which left many of the red rocks of Cheshire, could be explained only by a vast movement of a continent of which northern England formed a very small part. Such movements of continents took place slowly, at rates probably varying from 1 to 10cm a year, and they are still taking place now. Continental movement is now part of the broader subject of plate tectonics which has recently received considerable popular exposition, for instance in science programmes produced for television. There are also a number of books ranging from popular and school textbook accounts (e.g. Press and Siever, 1982) to summaries of recent developments in plate tectonics for students and research workers (see References). Plate tectonics deal with the fate of sediments deposited on the margins of plates as well as with the effects of crustal stretching or tension, for example in the Great Rift Valley and Red Sea today.

In this introduction we cover mainly the time between the formation of the earliest rocks in the area, the Dinantian (Table 1), and the end of the Triassic (Table 4). We refer to the major factors which controlled sedimentation or affected it, that is the formation of nearly all the rocks in our area of northwest England. These include the sources of the sediments and the manner in which they were later preserved up to the time in which the rocks reached their present structure. The period covered by these events is just over 350 million years, but that of the deposition of the rocks probably measures just under 100 million years (see the Geological Column Leaflet — Eagar, 1985, where shorter intervals of time are recorded with past latitudes of the general area of England and the times and names of the major episodes of mountain-making orogenies).

Dinantian (Lower Carboniferous) (Table 1)
During the Dinantian and through most of later Silesian time northern England lay in a depositional area subject to regional north-south tension (rifting), with the result that a series of crustal blocks developed, bounded by northwest – southeast and northeast – southwest faults. These blocks tended to behave independently, some slightly tilting, others sinking relatively rapidly to form 'lows', which were filled with thick sequences of clastic sediments. Yet other tended to remain stable or sank very little, to form 'highs' which tended to retain thinner covers of sediments and to include more slowly formed rocks, such as limestones. The Craven area to the north contained a number of 'highs', with thin successions, and also extensive 'lows' (see Itinerary II, Figure 3). The evolution of this area has been discussed by Gawthorpe, *et al*. 1989.

Table 1. Subdivisions of the Dinantian.
(after Arthurton, *et al*, 1988 and Aitkenhead, *et al*, 1985)

Stage	Craven Basin	North Derbyshire
Brigantian	Lower Bowland Shales	Longstone Mudstones Eyam Limestones Monsal Dale Limestones
Asbian	Pendleside Limestone	Bee Low Limestones
Holkerian	Worston Shales	Woo Dale Limestones
Arundian		~~~~~
Chadian	Thornton Limestone Thornton Shales-with-Limestone	
Ivorian	Chatburn Limestone	

In the Derbyshire area there was a Dinantian 'high' which extended over the area covered by Itinerary I. Early Dinantian history is not well known because strata of this age are not exposed. However, we know that the irregular basement topography was completely flooded by the Holkerian (Table 1). During Ashian time a depositional slope developed around the Derbyshire platform (Figure 1, southeast corner) where shelf limestones were laid down and where corals and brachiopods were abundant (Broadhurst, in Broadhurst *et al.*, 1970).

From late Holkerian to early Brigantian time sporadic widespread volcanic activity took place. Basic sills, basalt lava flows, broken-up volcanic debris (pyroclastics) and several volcanic vents have long been known (see Arnold-Bemrose, 1907). The location of the activity was evidently controlled by the structure of the basement blocks on which the sediments accumulated (Gawthorpe, *et al.* 1987).

Silesian (Upper Carboniferous) (Table 2).
By contrast with the limestones forming the bulk of the Dinantian, clay rocks and sandstones predominate throughout the Silesian with subordinate carbonates and beds of coal, the latter much increasing in number and thickness with the onset of the Westphalian. Marine and non-marine fossils are abundant but restricted to thin bands, and rich floras are found usually only in the stratal vicinity of seams of coal, especially above them. This wide range of fossils has facilitated correlation and classification (Table 2). Goniatites have proved particularly useful stratigraphical indicators, especially in the Namurian, where marine bands are common. At higher levels, in the Westphalian, shells of non-marine bivalves and plants, both clearly identifiable fossil remains (macroplants) and miospores (spores and pollen less than 200 μm in diameter), have proved invaluable. In the classification of the Silesian currently in use (much abbreviated in Table 2) the boundaries at the base and at the top of the Namurian have been placed at arbitrarily chosen marine bands. These extend over very wide areas within and outside the British Isles and are readily recognisable.

The Namurian (formerly the Millstone Grit Series of the Pennine area) passes up into the Westphalian (formerly the Coal Measures). The top of the Westphalian is everywhere incomplete in northern England. The Namurian sediments accumulated as a broad north-south lobe which coincides roughly with the location of the present Pennines, their main outcrop. These sediments reach a maximum thickness of 2km (over 6,500 feet), which is found in the Rossendale area, north of Manchester (Figure 1). Away from the Pennines the Namurian succession is generally buried beneath younger rocks, but is known to become much thinner from the evidence of numerous boreholes and seismic profiles obtained in recent years during the course of hydrocarbon exploration.

Table 2. Classification of the British Silesian.
(after Ramsbottom, *et al*, 1978)

Series	Stage	Goniatite Index	Selected marine bands	Selected non-marine faunal belts	Miospore zones
STEPHANIAN	Stephanian				
	Cantabrian				
WESTPHALIAN	Westphalian D				XI
	Westphalian C		*Anthracoceras cambriense*		X
			Anthracoceras aegiranum		IX
	Westphalian B				VIII
			Anthracoceras vanderbeckei	cristagalli	VII
	Westphalian A		*Gastrioceras listeri*		VI
		G_2			
			Gastrioceras subcrenatum	fallax-protea	SS
NAMURIAN	Yeadonian	G_1	*Gastrioceras cumbriense*		FR
			Gastrioceras cancellatum		
	Marsdenian	R_2			
			Reticuloceras gracile		KV
	Kinder-scoutian	R_1			
	Alportian	H_2			
	Chokierian	H_1			SO
	Arnsbergian	E_2			TR
	Pendelian	E_1			NC
			Cravenoceras leion		

Index goniatites
G Gastrioceras
R Reticuloceras
H Homoceras
E Eumorphoceras

In the Manchester area the bulk of the Namurian is made of sandstones, often coarse-grained, and clayrocks with subordinate siltstones and occasional limestones and coal beds. The sandstones are generally rich in feldspar and quartz grains and exhibit cross-stratification (both trough and planar) indicating past current directions, commonly from the north and northeast and less commonly from the south and west. They often contain an abundance of drifted plants. The sediments are interpreted as delta sequences mostly draining land to the north and northeast (from what is now Scotland and beyond it, to Scandinavia), with less important sources from the south and southeast (St. George's Land). Most of the clayrocks of the Namurian were probably deposited in lakes and lagoons, as flood basin sediments.

In Pendelian and Lower Kinderscoutian times (Table 2) the deltas advanced from the north into deep water where turbidites were formed by frequent downflows of turbidity currents carrying sediments in front of the deltaic slope (Collinson, 1976). Such turbidites (which are not included within any of the routes described in this guide) form the bottom of sequences which are hundreds of metres thick, each showing, in general, an upward coarsening in grain size, for instance on Pendle Hill (Itinerary II). Later deltaic sequences tend to be thinner, but reach tens of metres in thickness. They again consist of upwardly coarsening sediments and have at their tops many erosive channels filled with coarse-grained sediments (river channel fills). In many cases the channels have been found to be of low-sinuosity type, suggesting the development of braidplains such as now form in association with high discharge, weak banked distributaries (Bristow, 1988). In many of these later shallow water deltas the deposits were laid down in sheet-like form (Itinerary IV, the Rough Rock) whereas in others they were distributed in an elongate fashion similar to the bar-fingers of the birdsfoot delta which has formed at the mouth of the modern Mississippi (see Itinerary III, Haslingden Flags). The coarsening-upwards sequences, each of which represents the advance of a delta front, are usually capped by rootlet horizons and thin seams of coal. They, in turn, are typically overlain by a thin marine band indicating an invasion of the sea over a very wide area, probably the result of an eustatic rise in sea-level (Rambottom, 1981). Deltas then began to build out once more into the sea.

The Namurian deltaic sediments rarely contain body fossils such as occur in the interbedded fully marine bands, but accumulation often proceeded fast enough for the preservation of trace fossils reflecting activity by burrowing organisms. These traces have been found for instance on the tops of turbidites, on the delta slope where an origin by a different fauna is indicated, and on the delta top where the trace assemblages are again different (Eagar, *et al.*, 1985). They indicate, in middle and late Namurian times, progressive colonisation of deltaic environments by marine molluscs, especially bivalves, "worms" and arthropods.

There is evidence that in the Pennine Namurian basin subsidence was not uniform. Some local facies and thickness changes are most readily explained in terms of basement control, particularly movements on faulted blocks beneath the Namurian cover (Collinson, 1988). These movements represent a continuation of those affecting deposition during Dinantian times.

During the succeeding Westphalian, continued crustal subsidence allowed the accumulation of a thick sequence of sediments in northwest England, reaching more than 2km (*c.* 7000 ft) south of Manchester (Taylor, *et al.*, 1963). Subsidence was again accompanied by significant movements of basement faults, producing lateral thickness and facies changes and also splits and unions of coal seams (Bromehead, *et al.*, 1933; Broadhurst & France, 1986; Chisholm, 1990).

The incoming of the Westphalian marks a gradual increase upward in fluvial and swampy alluvial flat conditions throughout the entire Pennine area. Fluvial and boggy lake sediments become more commonplace and the development of channel-fill sands is much less widespread in comparison with the Namurian. Coal beds become more numerous and include many thicker seams interspersed with thinner coarsening-upwards sequences. Sandstones are thinner.

In the lower third of Westphalian A thin marine bands are common and very widespread within the Pennine region, but then they decrease in quantity and areal extent upward (Calver, 1969) until they are absent in the remainder of Westphalian A. They are occasionally present, proving very useful stratigraphic markers, from the base of Westphalian B to the middle of Westphalian C (Table 2).

The depositional setting of the Westphalian was thus a continuation of late Namurian times, but with increasing emphasis on very widespread alluvial swamps, forming on the delta top and towards the hinterland, and on uniformity of physical conditions. The nature of the sediments continued as before, but in the lower Westphalian began to include green mudrocks with little detrital mica and increased chlorite, evidently derived from the west (Chisholm, 1990). Interdistributary bays and lagoons, the sites of deposition from river levee overwash and breaching (crevasse-splay) were colonised by non-marine faunas, notably in the intervals where decaying plant matter was abundant. These were commonly of bivalves and fish, and less often included small arthropods, such as small king-crabs, ostracods and estheriids. Towards the top of the Westphalian in the Manchester area the Ardwick

Group includes freshwater limestones. If beds younger than those of the Ardwick Group were deposited in this area they have been subsequently removed by erosion.

Hercynian plate convergence and orogeny

Permo-Triassic deposits rest on an erosion surface formed mainly on Carboniferous sediments of various ages. This indicates that Carboniferous basin subsidence was followed by uplift of 2-3km, sufficient to bring to the surface coals of bituminous rank. The uplift was accompanied by extensive fold and fault movements, sometimes, if not always, involving the activation of earlier faults. These post-Carboniferous earth movements, due mainly to north-south compression and block jostling, are local expressions of the Asturic orogenic phase of the Hercynian, which affected a region extending from South Wales and southwest England through to the Netherlands and northern Germany (Harz Mountains).

Permo-Triassic

The compressive Hercynian movements may have lasted into the Permian. Soon, however, east-west intra-plate tension was again established and this reactivation gave rise to basinal subsidence along faults aligned roughly north-south. The Permo-Triassic Cheshire-Shropshire Basin is one of many such basins and is very strongly fault-bounded to the east. The crustal stretching was associated with the eventual opening of the Atlantic in Cretaceous times.

The end of the Permian Period was marked by a world-wide lowering of sea-level to a minimum, perhaps lower than at any time since the Precambrian, with the result that, irrespective of regional uplift, many shallow shelf seas became continental area. All through the Carboniferous-Permian time 'England' was moving northward, well into the arid belt of the northern hemisphere.

The latest Permian and earliest Triassic beds do not contain fossiliferous sequences by which the Triassic beds can be separated from those of the Permian (see Table 4). The difficulty is circumvented by using the term Permo-Triassic and in this brief introduction much unquestionable Triassic is included under the same heading.

Permo-Triassic palaeoenvironments varied widely in space and time, even within the Manchester area. The Lower Permian Collyhurst Sandstone formed in a sand-sea which contained dry interdune areas, dunes and very large sand dunes (draa) brought into being by a steady easterly trade wind. The Collyhurst Sandstone was succeeded locally by the Manchester Marls (Table 4), which formed in an arm of the sea — the Bakevellia Sea — which supported a small impoverished fauna, mainly of gastropods and bivalves, under conditions of varying salinity, including hypersalinity. The Manchester Marls are at present unexposed, but examples of their lithology and fauna are well displayed in the Stratigraphical Hall of the Manchester Museum.

The succeeding Chester Pebble Bed Formation (Table 4) represents at first a response to increased uplift of the land and indicates a period of very high discharge of a braided river system, the channels having low sinuosities. The gradually decreasing grain size and different sedimentary structures of the succeeding Wilmslow Sandstone Formation show that fluvial discharge and influences gradually died away as aeolian processes took over. The area was again elevated and eroded at the end of Scythian (Lower Triassic) times (Table 4) and the sequence of river to wind deposits was repeated in the Helsby Sandstone Formation. Later basinal deposits of the Mercia Mudstone Group reveal occasional intertidal episodes with trace fossils (Ireland *et al.*, 1978), hypersaline lagoons and salinas with marine input, as the landscape became worn down. The predominantly arid conditions of the Permo-Triassic rocks of the Cheshire Basin are fully described not only in Table 4 but also within the description of Itineraries VIII to XI and need no further elaboration here. Footprints of reptiles, for example *Chirotherium and Rhynchosaurus*, provide spectacular fossils and are by no means confined to single horizons (see specimens in the Manchester Museum), but no skeletons of the former have been seen. It is still possible to find footprints, whose locations need to be conserved with the greatest care. The 'print' is invariably a cast in sandstone which has filled the original print made in soft incoherent clay rock (commonly misnamed marl). It needs to be stressed, however, that in general remains of life in the Trias are rare. Occasional plants, spores, estheriids, insect wings and arthropod tracks have been found in the Cheshire Plain (see Itinerary X, p.79). Triassic fossils are generally associated with interbedded sandy-clay rocks of fluvial or intertidal origin.

Taken together, the Permo-Triassic sediments of the Manchester area reach a maximum thickness of about 4km (over 13,000 feet) and so indicate a remarkable degree of subsidence of the crust in central and eastern Cheshire. Rise of worldwide sea-levels towards the end of the Triassic Period brought about a marine transgression, which is evidenced in the fossiliferous Rhaetic beds of the Prees outlier, south of the Manchester Guide area.

Jurassic - Tertiary time.

Both the extensional basinal subsidence and the marine transgression of the later Triassic continued into the Jurassic Period. Deposits up to Middle Liassic age occur in the Prees area of south Cheshire and Shropshire. There is then a gap in the geological record of the Manchester area up to the middle of the Tertiary Period. It is likely that deposition continued during parts of Jurassic, Cretaceous and Tertiary times, but such deposits have been removed during subsequent periods of erosion. Sediments of Miocene-Pliocene age are known in the Peak District and Tertiary dykes are known from localities in north Shropshire, north Staffordshire, in the Grindleton area north of Clitheroe and in the Eden Valley. The mineralisation of the area, involving copper, lead, cobalt, nickel and vanadium, is possibly Tertiary in age (Naylor, *et al*., 1989).

Pleistocene and Holocene

Much of the Manchester area is covered by a superficial layer of Pleistocene and younger Holocene deposits resting on a weathered surface, which in places is traversed by extensive channel systems, sometimes extending down to depths several tens of metres below present sea-level (Howell, 1973). The channels resulted from drainage when sea-level was very much lower than at present as a result of the extraction of water to form Polar and Sub-polar ice caps in the Pleistocene Period. The Pleistocene sediments include glacial tills ('boulder clay'), lacustrine deposits, some showing varves (rhythmic banding due to seasonal melting), fluvial sands and solifluction deposits ('head'). Almost all are of Devensian (late Pleistocene) age. Recent descriptions of these and of post-Pleistocene sediments are given by Johnson (1985).

Structure of the area around Manchester

Figure 1 represents a much simplified geological map showing the distribution of the 'solid' rocks (i.e. excluding all superficial deposits) of the Manchester area. East of Manchester the north-south trending Pennine Anticline is a broad arching structure, dipping more steeply to the west than to the east. It has been eroded to reveal a core of Dinantian limestones to the south, around Buxton, and to expose Namurian rocks in the centre and north of the anticline. Erosion of the NE-SW Clitheroe Anticline has similarly exposed a Dinantian core, whilst in the Rossendale Anticline, between Manchester and Clitheroe, the Namurian is again exposed.

Manchester itself lies on the rim of the Cheshire Basin, a structure which is associated with the contemporaneous major fault movements, especially along its eastern margin. It is flanked to the north by the Rossendale Anticline and to the east by the Pennine Anticline and is rimmed by Westphalian rocks of the Lancashire and Cheshire coalfields, whilst the central region is occupied by the Permo-Trias.

In the foregoing pages we have outlined the broad geological history of the Manchester area since the beginning of Carboniferous time. We have emphasised particularly the change from region tension and basin subsidence, with heavy sedimentation, during Carboniferous time to compression and substantial uplift at the end of the Carboniferous Period and into the Permo-Triassic. Such a reversal of tectonic trend is known as inversion. The compression was a part of the Hercynian orogeny which, over the globe as a whole, resulted in the union of most, if not all of the continental crust into a 'supercontinent' — Pangaea II. The establishment of this vast continent brought with it a drop in sea-level and major climatic changes, which are reflected in the nature of the Permo-Triassic sediments. After the formation of Pangaea II, continental break-up and especially the opening of the Atlantic brought about crustal tension in the Manchester area once more and created the basins which accommodated thick Permo-Triassic successions. The geological record of events between the early Jurassic and Pleistocene is poor in the Manchester region. However, evidence elsewhere indicates that in this time interval Britain (and northern Europe as a whole) moved progressively into higher latitudes, thus bringing it within range of glaciation during the Pleistocene Epoch.

ITINERARY I

Wye Dale Area, east of Buxton

A. E. Adams

Ordnance Survey 1:50,000 Sheet 119; 1:25,000 SK07/17
British Geological Survey 1:50,000 Sheet 111

Some of the oldest exposed rocks in north Derbyshire are found in the Woo Dale inlier, east of Buxton. This itinerary includes localities in these Holkerian limestones as well as in some of the younger sediments. Although many lithostratigraphical names have been used for the Derbyshire Dinantian, Aitkenhead and Chisholm (1982) proposed a standardised nomenclature with one set of names applicable throughout north Derbyshire (Table 1).

The Wye Dale area, close to the A6, is easily accessible from Manchester by private or public transport. The itinerary has been extended to include a classic nearby exposure in Carboniferous basaltic igneous rocks.

Route. Take the A6 from Buxton which follows the River Wye eastwards. About 2.5km after leaving Buxton you pass under the first railway bridge. 200m beyond, on the north side of the road lies the entrance to Cunning Dale (SK 084725). It is usually possible to park a car at the entrance to the dale. If not, cars can be left at the Devonshire Arms (Figure 2). In this area the lower portion of the Woo Dale Limestones is dolomitized and locally known as the Woo Dale Dolomite. Small exposures near the entrance to Cunning Dale (**Locality 1**) show typical brown crystalline dolomites. In places the dolomite has been calcitised as a result of weathering, either at the present day or much earlier perhaps as a result of post-Hercynian uplift. The product is a dark vuggy rock of crystalline calcite.

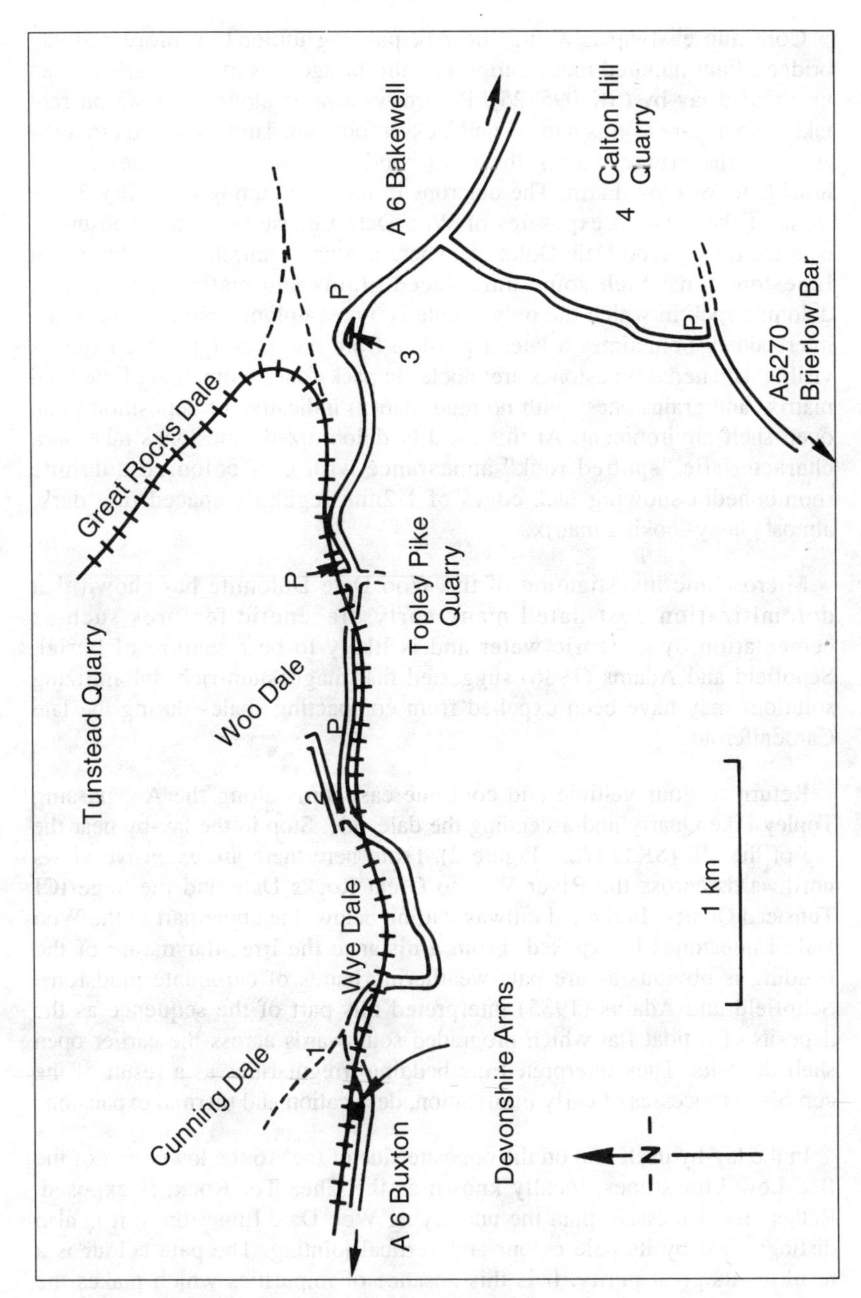

Figure 2. Wye Dale area, locality map, east of Buxton.

Continue eastwards along the A6, passing under two more railway bridges. Four hundred metres after the third bridge cars may be parked in an unsurfaced lay-by (SK 095725). Return westwards along the road on foot taking great care as it is narrow and lacks a footpath. Turn right and cross the river by the bridge, taking the right hand track which continues up the hillside to Woolow Farm. The outcrops in the road cutting (**Locality 2**) are some of the cleanest exposures of Woo Dale Limestones. The exposure is near the top of Woo Dale Dolomite where unaltered limestones, dolomitized limestones in which some unreplaced grains and matrix remain, and dolomite rock in which the only calcite is a post-dolomitization cement, are interbedded. Sometimes a lateral passage from one rock type to another is visible. Unaltered limestones are bioclastic packstones (containing little mud matrix) and grainstones (with no mud matrix) indicative of deposition in an open shelf environment. At this locality dolomitized limestones take on a characteristic "spotted rock" appearance with buff-coloured dolomite rhombohedra showing face edges of 1-2mm regularly-spaced in a dark, almost glassy-looking matrix.

Microscopic investigation of the Woo Dale Dolomite has shown that dolomitization post-dated many early diagenetic features such as cementation by meteoric water and is likely to be a feature of burial. Schofield and Adams (1986) suggested that magnesium-rich dolomitizing solutions may have been expelled from compacting shales during the late Carboniferous.

Return to your vehicle and continue eastwards along the A6, passing Topley Pike Quarry and ascending the dale side. Stop in the lay-by near the top of the hill (SK113725, Figure 2). From here there are extensive views northwards across the River Wye to Great Rocks Dale and the huge ICI Tunstead Quarry. In the old railway cutting below, the upper part of the Woo Dale Limestones is exposed. From a distance the irregular nature of the bedding is obvious as are pale-weathering bands of carbonate mudstone. Schofield and Adams (1985) interpreted this part of the sequence as the deposits of a tidal flat which prograded southwards across the earlier open shelf deposits. They interpreted the bedding irregularities as a result of the combined processes of early lithification, desiccation and thermal expansion.

In the lay-by itself and on the opposite side of the A6 the lower part of the Bee Low Limestones, locally known as the Chee Tor Rock, is exposed. Rather more massive than the underlying Woo Dale Limestones, it is also distinguished by its pale colour and vertical jointing. The pale colour is a result of its great purity. It is this absence of impurities which makes the Chee Tor Rock a valuable resource and is the main reason for the development of the ICI quarry at Tunstead. The sediment is well seen at the western entrance to the lay-by (**Locality 3**). Pale, fairly fine-grained bioclastic limestones are separated by irregular stylolitic surfaces (complex zig-zag lines) seen here in plan and section. Good examples of the sponge? *Chaetetes* are found towards the top of the stepped face.

Shortly beyond the lay-by take the right turn on the the A5270. Parking is available on the sharp bend just over 1km from the junction (SK 112709). From here walk to Calton Hill Quarry where basic volcanics at the top of the Bee Low Limestones are exposed. Parts of the original quarry face have been preserved and the locality has been designated an SSSI by English Nature (the Nature Conservancy Council). It is owned by Derbyshire County Council and permission to visit must be obtained from the County Planning Officer, County Offices, Matlock, Derbyshire, DE4 3AG. The permit includes a map showing the access route to the quarry on foot from the A5270.

The history of this site and a detailed account of the present SSSI have been given by Miller (1988). There is still controversy over whether there are one or two phases of igneous activity represented at Calton Hill. The majority view is that there were two phases — the eruption of basaltic lavas first, accompanied by tuffs and agglomerates. This took place during the Asbian on a surface of Bee Low Limestones, and was followed at a later date by intrusion of a basanitic (silica poor, alkali basalt) magma which seems to have utilised the older basaltic vents as it approached the surface. These two types of activity are well seen in the SSSI which is centred around the pool. Tuffs are not well exposed, but patches of grey-green rock containing limestone fragments can be found. On the south side of the pool the older amygdaloidal basalts are cut by irregular sheets of dense, relatively fresh, fine-grained intrusive basanite. This latter material, representing the second phase of activity, is famous for its small nodules of ultrabasic rocks made up of the minerals spinel, olivine, orthopyroxene and clinopyroxene. These have been interpreted as fragments of uppermost mantle carried up by the basanite magma from its source region. The locality is also known for small geodes which contain a variety of minerals including amethyst. *Collecting is not allowed without permission from English Nature.*

Complex relationships between vesicular and amygdaloidal basalts, which are heavily altered, and the much less altered later intrusives are also seen north of the pool. Columnar jointing in various orientations is also visible and is best-developed in a horizontal basanite unit on the eastern edge of the pool.

ITINERARY II

Clitheroe and Pendle Hill

I. M. Simpson

Ordnance Survey 1:50,000 Sheet 103; 1:25,000 SK64/74
British Geological Survey 1:63,360 Sheet 68; 1,25,000 SO 74

The busy market town of Clitheroe in the Ribble Valley is dominated, as it has been for centuries, by the ancient and now ruined Norman castle (SD 744117) in the town centre. The castle, standing high on a knoll of Lower Carboniferous limestone, commands a wide view of the valley and surrounding districts, thus forming a very appropriate starting-point for this itinerary, which can occupy a full day.

A broad, denuded anticline with a NE-SW axis controls the distribution of rocks in this part of the Ribble Valley. Shales, mudstones and limestones of Dinantian age occupy the floor of the valley with escarpments of the overlying Namurian sandstones forming the flanking ridges of high ground, Pendle Hill to the southeast and the Forest of Bowland to the northwest (Figure 3). Clitheroe and Pendle Hill lie on the southeastern limb of the anticline.

Details of the succession are as follows:

	metres
PENDLE GRIT	
Thickly-bedded, coarse-grained sandstone	250
UPPER BOWLAND SHALE	
Dark grey shales with thin bands of dark grey limestone	150
PENDLESIDE SANDSTONE	
Thick beds of sandstone separated by thin bands of shale	100
LOWER BOWLAND SHALE	
Dark grey mudstone with thin bands of dark limestone	100
PENDLESIDE LIMESTONE	
Thick beds of light grey limestone with thin shale partings	80
WORSTON SHALE GROUP	
Dark grey calcareous shale and mudstone with thin layers of dark limestone	300

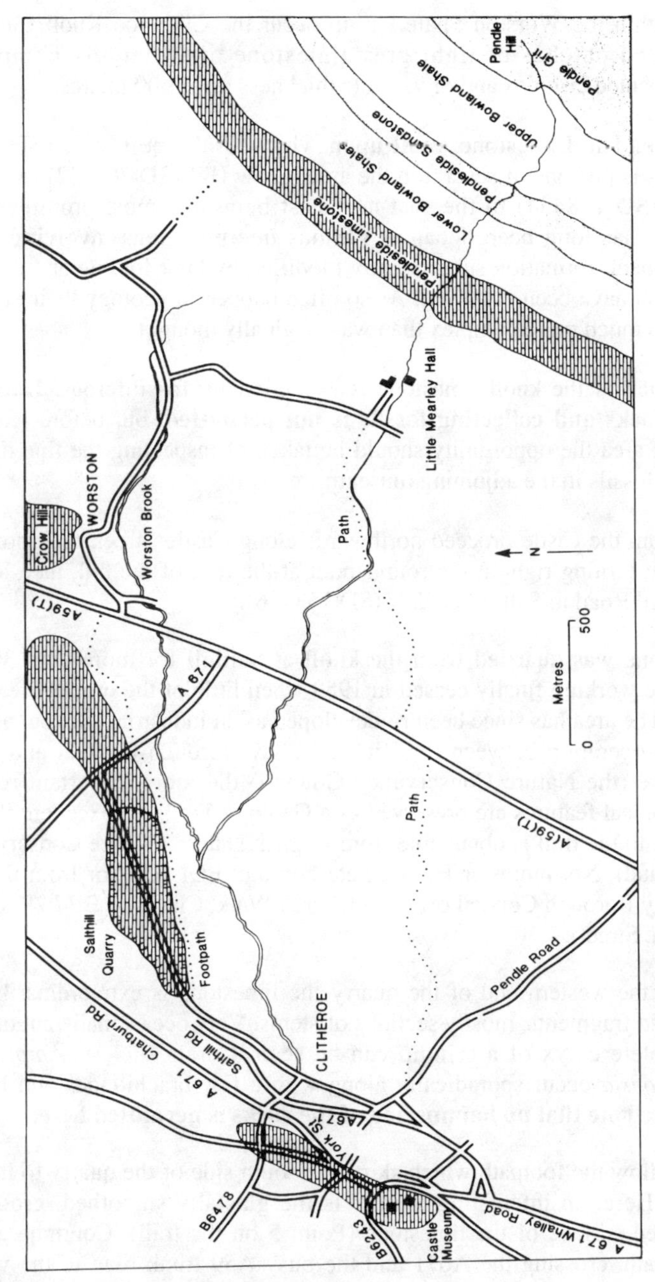

Figure 3. Clitheroe and Pendle Hill, Lancashire.

Within the Worston Shale Group occur the Clitheroe Knoll Limestones, isolated patches of light grey limestone often largely composed of fragmented crinoids and of variable thickness up to 600 metres.

Route. The Limestone knoll upon which Clitheroe Castle (SD 742417) stands is just one of several in the area, Crow Hill (SD 769432) and Worsaw Hill (SD 778434) to the east-northeast being the most prominent. Their origin has long been debated. Various interpretations involving reef and shell-bank formation subsequently modified by later folding and differential erosion have been proposed. As so often happen in geology their origin now seems much more complex than was originally thought.

Much of the knoll limestone is exceptionally fossiliferous. **Hammering the rocks and collecting fossils is not permitted,** but before leaving the castle area the opportunity should be taken of inspecting the fine display of local fossils in the adjoining museum.

From the castle proceed northwards along Castle Street, then down York Street, turning right at the roundabout at the foot of the hill, then left along Salthill Road to Salthill Quarry (SD 753426).

Stone was quarried from the knoll at Salthill for more than 300 years before working finally ceased in 1959 when little of the original feature was left. The area has since been re-developed as an industrial site, but as a result of co-operation between the Ribble Valley Borough Council and English Nature (the Nature Conservancy Council) the more important remaining geological features are preserved as a Geology Trail. An excellent illustrated guide to the trail is obtainable from English Nature (Nature Conservancy for England), Northminster House, Peterborough PE1 IUA. or from the Ribble Valley Borough Council office in Church Walk, Clitheroe BB7 2RA (just off Castle Street).

At the western end of thc quarry the limestone is extraordinarily rich in crinoid fragments, mostly sections of stems. Very occasionally a more or less complete calyx of a crinoid can be seen. Corals such as *Amplexus* and *Emmonsia* occur sporadically along with a few brachiopods and blastoids. **Please note that no hammering of the rocks is permitted here.**

Follow the footpath which skirts the south side of the quarry to its eastern end. Here, an interesting feature is the glacially smoothed, grooved and striated surface of the limestone (Point 5 on the trail). Continue along the footpath, crossing the A671 and the busy A59 trunk road to the village of Worston (SD 769428); from there take the Downham road. For much of the way this road runs parallel with the Worston Brook in which, here and there, dark grey shale and mudstone of the Worston Shale Group are exposed. On reaching a T-junction (SD 780427) at which the Downham road bears left, turn to the right up a lane sign-posted ‘cul-de-sac’, and follow this lane in the direction of Pendle Hill. It soon deteriorates to a rough track and eventually ends at the foot of a markedly steeper slope down which a deeply cut gully descends. Except in very wet weather this gully is dry and displays a fine section of the upper strata of the Worston Shale Group and the overlying Pendleside Limestone.The limestone is fine-grained and contains numerous nodules of black chert, but few fossils other than small crinoid ossicles.

From the top of the gully cross a wide stretch of gently sloping, poorly drained moorland which, in the absence of exposures, is assumed to be underlain by Bowland Shales and Pendleside Sandstone, and ascend the steep escarpment formed by the Pendle Grit by means of a track which runs diagonally up to the right. From the flat, boulder-strewn summit of Pendle Hill a spectacular view is obtained across the Ribble Valley to the Forest of Bowland beyond.

The return from Pendle Hill can be made by descending into the deep clough formed by the Mearley Brook and joining the footpath which follows the brook to Little Mearley Hall (SD 775417). The rock succession is well exposed in this section with, at the top, thick beds of Pendle Grit sandstone forming a series of waterfalls.

Below the Pendle Grit the Upper Bowland Shale is well exposed and a careful search soon reveals that some of the beds are abundantly fossiliferous with the bivalves *Posidonia* and *Dunbarella*, and the goniatites *Cravenoceras* and *Eumorphoceras*. This fauna indicates that the upper part of the Upper Bowland Shale is of Namurian age, while the lower part is of Dinantian age.

Outcrops of Pendleside Sandstone and Lower Bowland Shale occur lower down the section and in the wood above Little Mearley Hall there are small quarries in the Pendleside Limestone. From Little Mearley Hall the return to Clitheroe can be made by a footpath through the fields or by road via Worston.

INTINERARY III

Cheesden Brook and Turf Moor

F. M. Broadhurst

Ordnance Survey 1:50,000 Sheet 109; 1:25,000 SD 81/91
British Geological Survey 1:63,360 Sheet 76

This excursion is best done by use of private transport. A convenient parking place for several cars or one or two minibuses is to be found on the south side of the A680 where it crosses Cheesden Brook (SD 822166). The excursion follows a 3km round trip across rough ground and high moor. Adequate clothing and footwear is essential and parties should be aware of the risk of being caught in mist. The Yeadonian (Namurian) rocks to be seen, however, are well exposed and worth the effort. There is much evidence of former industrial activity hereabouts and those interested are referred to Sandiford and Ashworth (1983). Further details of the geology are to be found in Bristow (1988), Wignall, (1987) and Wright, *et al.*, (1927).

Route. From the car park follow the A680 for about 200 metres towards the east (Rochdale direction) and turn left as soon as the cottages on the left hand side of the road are reached. Pass through the stile, then leave the path and bear left to reach the numerous low heaps of colliery waste about 200 metres away (Figure 4, **Locality 1**, SD 823167).

The mine tips are composed mainly of carbonaceous clayrock fragments with the occasional tough clay ironstone concretion. These rocks were derived from shaft sinkings to the Holcombe Brook Coal. Diligent search might reveal fossils from the Gastrioceras cancellatum Marine Band. The criss-cross (cancellate) ornament of the goniatite G. *cancellatum* is distinctive. Adjacent to the tips are old shafts capped by concrete slabs with iron grills. The direction of the air flow through these grills depends on atmospheric pressure. With rising pressure air flows into the shafts and old workings, with falling pressure air flows out. Follow the line of tips northwards.

In the bank above the reservoir, (Figure 4, **Locality 2**, SD 824170) remnants of the worked Holcombe Brook Coal (thickness about 0.3m) can be seen together with its floor. The coal is banded (due to the association of different coal types, vitrain, fusain, clarain and durain). the dominant joint system (cleat) of the coal is well shown and trends southeast-northwest. The siltstones and sandstones below the coal are badly weathered but yield

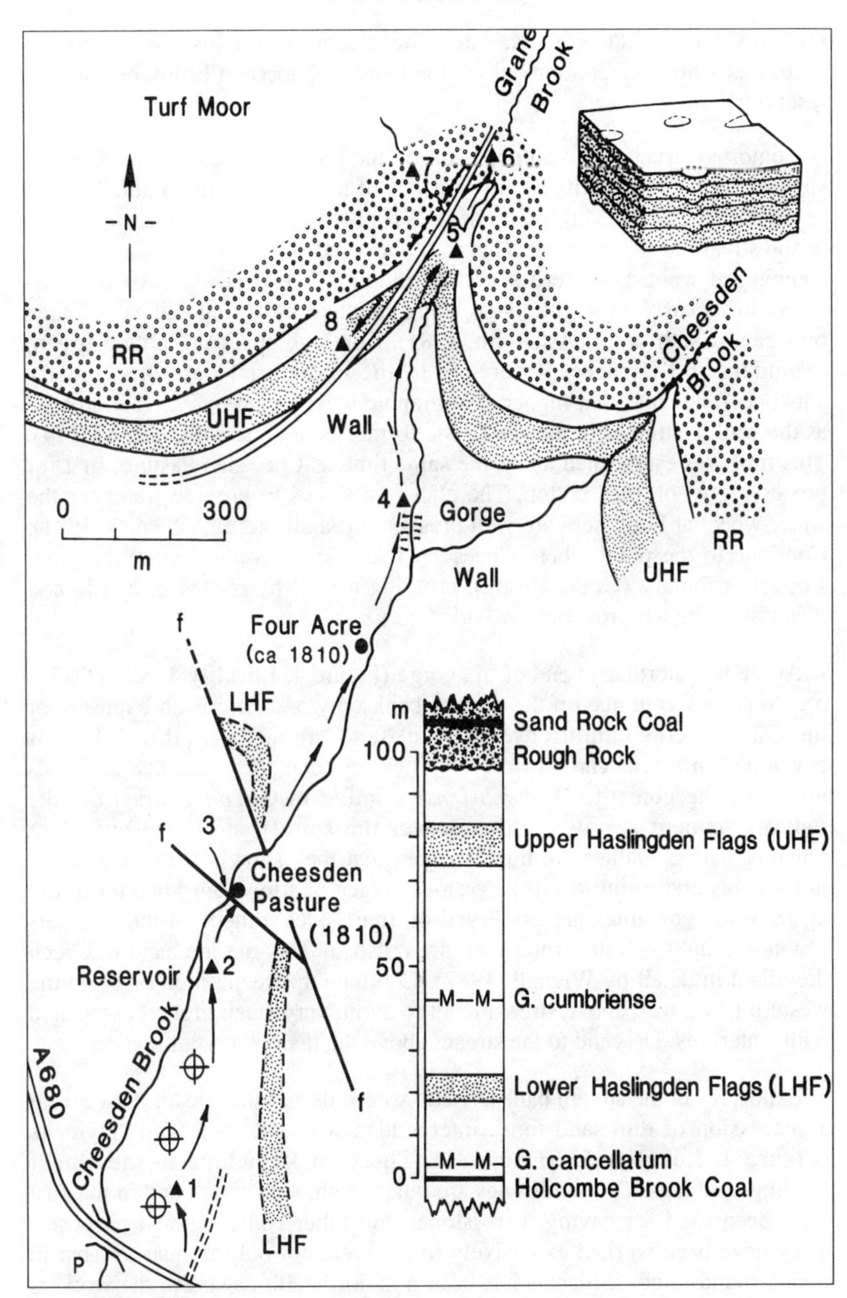

Figure 4. Turf Moor area.

recognisable rootlet remains. These beds represent a fossil soil and are known as seatearth. Continue along the bank of Cheesden Brook beyond the reservoir.

Contorted structures in an exposure on the opposite (western) bank of the stream (Figure 4, **Locality 3**) are evidence of the presence of a fault. The site of Cheesden Pasture Mill, built about 1810, is to be seen on the eastern bank of the stream at this locality. This mill was used intially for the carding and spinning of wool, but later for cotton spinning. It was powered by a water-wheel in its early days (the lodge being supplied by spring water) and then by steam (Sandiford & Ashworth, 1981). Continue upstream, noting stream meanders and terraces. Reference to the occasional outcrops (mostly siltstones) indicates that higher stratigraphic levels are progressively crossed as the walk continues to the site of the former Four Acre Mill, (SD 828174). This mill was established about the same time as Cheesden Pasture, first for processing wool, then cotton. The elaborate works to provide water for the water-wheel at Four Acre are well preserved (Sandiford & Ashworth, 1981). Continue to the point where Cheesden Brook divides and follow the more westerly tributary (Grane Brook), crossing a wall by means of a stile and then traversing a narrow but low-sided gorge.

At the top (northerly) end of the gorge (Figure 4, **Locality 4**, SD 829177) rock outcrops continue on the eastern bank only and here is an exposure of the Gastrioceras cumbriense Marine Band, about 0.4m thick. This is developed in black (carbon-rich) clayrock and contains a variety of fossils including the goniatite G. *cumbriense* (similar to G. *cancellatum* but the radial ornament is now dominant over the spiral) and numerous plant remains. The goniatites are interesting in that they show a wide size range, presumably indicating death at various stages of life, from juvenile to old aged. Some goniatites are preserved on their sides, others on their venters ("standing up") — but virtually all are crushed. This marine band has been described in detail by Wignall (1987). Continue upstream, preferably on the western bank, well above stream level to avoid very steep ground associated with waterfalls. Descend to the stream above the main waterfall section.

Exposures in the stream banks, small waterfalls and the stream floor reveal a succession of thin sandstones interbedded with siltstones and clayrocks (Figure 4, **Locality 5**, SD829181). These rocks belong to the Upper Haslingden Flags. The sandstones are quartz-rich, very tough and in the past have been used for paving, kerb stones and other constructional purposes. They have been worked extensively in the area, not only in quarries, but in underground mines. Silicosis has been a major health hazard to the workers involved. Observe the abundant ripple-marked surfaces on the sandstones and associated trace fossils, notably escape shafts (Figure 4, inset, right). The escape shafts are generally associated with the activity of bivalves which lived within the sediment but needed to maintain contact with the overlying water (via siphons) for their source of oxygen and (particulate) food. As sedimentation proceeded the bivalves were obliged to move upwards to maintain contact with their oxygen and food source. Escape shafts tend to be of about the same width at any one horizon, suggesting the presence, normally, of only one age-group (generation) of shells. Widths vary between horizons. Occasionally there is evidence of two generations. In this section no evidence has yet been seen of the bivalves presumed to be responsible for the escape structure. Elsewhere, however, escape shafts in similar rocks are found with bivalves preserved at the tops of the structures. The Upper Haslingden Flags have been interpreted as delta-front deposits, (Bristow, 1988). Continue upstream. A conspicuous face of sandstone marks the top of the steep-sided valley. This sandstone, the Rough Rock, is a pebbly, feldspathic arkosic sandstone (Figure 4, **Locality 6**). Plant remains, such as tree logs, can be seen. The sandstone is cross-stratified. It is probable that the Rough Rock accumulated in channels of an extensive delta-top distributary system, (Bristow, 1988).

At the sandstone exposure turn left (westwards) up the valley side to gain a rough roadway above (SD 830183). Here turn left (southwards), pass further exposures of the Rough Rock to reach a small stream flowing off Turf Moor. Follow this stream uphill, crossing extensive exposures of Rough Rock to **Locality 7** (SD 828182) where the seatearth of the Sand Rock Coal is well exposed. Return to the roadway and contine southwards to reach **Locality 8** (SD 828180) where there is an exposure of the Upper Haslingden Flags with load structures, formed when masses of sand about the size of tennis balls or footballs sank into yielding mud or silt beneath. Such structures are generally associated with rapid sedimentation. From this locality it is possible to return directly to the gorge and the site of Four Acre Mill and so return to the parking point.

ITINERARY IV

Chunal, Charlesworth and Broadbottom, near Glossop

Paul A. Selden

Ordnance Survey 1:50,000 Sheets 109 & 110;
1:25,000 Dark Peak Outdoor Leisure
British Geological Survey 1:50,000 Sheets 86 & 99

Glossop lies on the western limb of the Pennine Anticline, where the dipping and faulted succession of late Namurian and early Westphalian coarse-grained grits, sandstones and shales exert a profound influence on the topography. In particular, the geological control on Quaternary events, the resultant drainage patterns and industrial history can be readily appreciated. A full, clear day is ideal for this walk of about 15km, which starts at Glossop railway station and ends at Broadbottom station (Figure 5). There are frequent trains from Manchester Piccadilly to Glossop and Broadbottom, and there is ample parking at both stations. Alternatively, the excursion can be conveniently divided into two half-day circular walks from the stations. The excursion may be shortened by starting at the lay-by on the A624, 200m north of the Grouse Inn (SK 03459050), and omitting Locality 1.

Route. From Glossop Station, follow the A624 (Hayfield, Chapel-en-le-Frith) road south and after 1km, just as the road descends to the factory at Charlestown, notice Whiteley Nab to the southwest. The top of the Nab is formed of Chatsworth Grit (CG) dipping 12°W. The middle bench is produced by a sandstone, herein called the Hollingworth Head Rock (HR), and the lower bench, also dipping prominently westwards, is the upper leaf of the Kinderscout Grit (KG). The pile of stones on the lower bench was once a flue chimney from one of the mills seen in the valley bottom.

Continue down to cross the brook, pass the A6016 road junction, and in 100m cross the bridge over another stream and turn immediately left down a track which runs along a factory wall (SK 03389306). Follow this wall, ignoring the footbridge straight ahead, and cross Gnat Hole Brook by the second footbridge upstream. The flat bottom of the valley here is an old industrial floor. Looking southeast, the prominent tor on the skyline is the Worm Stones, a scarp of the lower leaf of KG; the brook being followed is a strike stream on the shales between the upper and lower KG. Upstream, the valley narrows considerably and its form suggests that of a glacial overflow channel. The presence of Lake District erratics in the stream bed indicates that boulder clay, which can be found up to 300m above sea-level in the

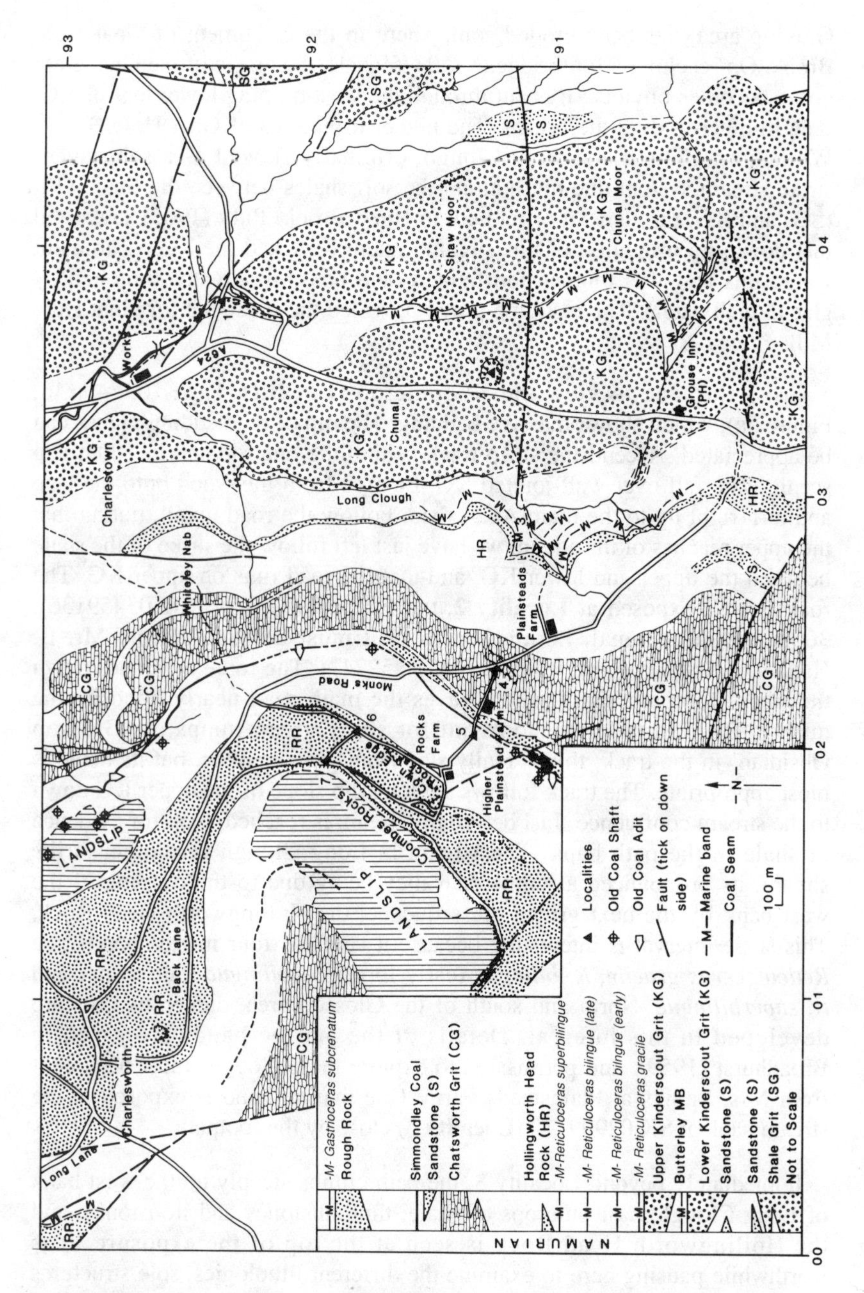

Figure 5a. Chunal and Charlesworth area.

Glossop area, has been eroded somewhere in the catchment of Gnat Hole Brook. On reaching a footbridge (SK 03759244), the origin of the Gnat Hole gorge becomes obvious; it is cut through the west-dipping lower leaf of KG, seen in outcrop over the bridge. The higher tributaries of Gnat Hole Brook, Whitethorn Clough and Bray Clough, originally flowed as a subsequent strike stream system due north along the soft shales between the Shale Grit (SG) and KG, through Moorfield col to Hurst Brook. Pitty (1965) suggested that down-dip migration of this stream system breached the KG escarpment where this leaf was thinner and faulted (and possibly already exploited by glacial meltwater). The resulting gorge provided the ideal site for Gnat Hole Mill.

Cross the lane to view the KG outcrop (**Locality 1**, SK 03749246, Figure 5a), which shows massive bedding. The dip of the bedding planes can be appreciated. Ascend the steep track behind the outcrop and in 100m is a scenic waterfall over well-jointed KG. Emerge from the wood onto the lane and turn right up to the main A624 road. Follow the road uphill, noting that the upper reaches of the stream we have just left follow the strike of the shale between the upper and lower KG, and that the road runs on upper KG. The rock is well exposed at **Locality 2**, the Fireplace Quarry (SK 03459136), 300m beyond Chunal. Permission to visit must be sought from Mr. B. Hallam of Shepley Farm, Chunal (0457 852747). The route continues down the track (footpath sign) which leaves the main road nearly opposite the quarry. Beyond the gate, look out for shiny green lumps of 'Glossop Obsidian' in the track; this is really slag from glass making, but its name is most appropriate. The track follows the long dip slope of the upper KG down to the stream confluence. Just before the stream is reached, look for evidence of shale in the path bank. The stream in Long Clough is another strike stream, its pronounced asymmetric valley being due to the capping of the west bank by the next grit in the sequence, the Hollingworth Head Rock. This shale interval is interesting because it contains four marine bands: the *Reticuloceras gracile*, *R. bilingue* (early form), *R. bilingue* (late form), and *R. superbilingue*. North and south of the Glossop area, numerous grits are developed in this interval. Details of the marine bands are given in Broadhurst (1959), and permission to explore these cloughs must be sought from Mrs. Spinks at Plainsteads Farm. One marine band is exposed in the stream bank at SK 02909110 (**Locality 3**) close by the footpath.

Immediately beyond Locality 3, the path climbs steeply up the west bank of Long Clough, past outcrops of shale, thin siltstones and ironstones, and the Hollingworth Head Rock is seen at the top of the exposure. It is worthwhile pausing here to examine the different lithologies, sole structures and the effect of the HR on the scenery. The path runs down the side of

Plainsteads to emerge on the Monks' Road. Turn right, and in 150m a lane on the left leads to Higher Plainstead Farm (goats' milk ice cream). Depressions in the ground seen over the walls on either side of the road are old stone quarries in the Chatsworth Grit. The CG is not mappable north of Glossop, where its place in the Namurian sequence is taken by the (Huddersfield White Rock, HWR; = Holcombe Brook Grit, HBG). From this junction (**Locality 4**, SK 02329123), the effect of westerly dipping grits on the scenery can be readily appreciated. The gently shelving ground due south, Matley Moor and due north, Whiteley Nab is formed on CG. Plainsteads and Hollingworth Head lie just above the HR scarp and further east the long Kinderscout Grit dip slopes (upper KG at the Grouse Inn) are prominent. To the west, Cown Edge dominates the skyline; this is the Rough Rock (RR), the topmost grit in the Namurian. Indentations in the scarp mark the positions of tear faults. Broadhurst (1959) suggested the col below and right of Plainsteads could be a glacial overflow channel from an ice margin lake over Glossop and running up Long Clough. 50m beyond Higher Plainstead Farm the track crosses a stream on the outcrop of the Simmondley Coal (**Locality 5**, SK 02069131). This 60cm thick seam was worked all along the outcrop, the only evidence here being the shale tips, an old sough and railway relics used in the track.

At Rocks Farm (SK 01949141) turn sharp right up the walled track to the stile. The view from here is highly instructive. To the east, the end of the Kinderscout plateau is formed of KG, which also forms the slope behind the Grouse Inn, and the dip slopes we have walked across are well displayed. In the far distant southeast, the Carboniferous Limestone of the White Peak is visible. The lower bench of Lantern Pike is formed of RR, and the summit and the long slope running down to Aspenshaw Hall is the Woodhead Hill Rock (WH). To the right of the Hall, the WH can be seen to curve upwards again; this is the beginning of the Goyt Syncline which ends spectacularly at the Roaches above Leek. Aspenshaw Hall lies on the axis. To the southwest, the complementary Todd Brook Anticline can also be seen, the most westerly slopes dipping west again. Follow the track to the right to two old quarries around SK 021918 (**Locality 6**). These show the massive nature of the RR. Search here for ripple marks, plant fossils and prominent rotten carbonate concretions.

A path between the two quarries crosses the Rough Rock outcrop to Coombes (**Locality 7**, SK 01949195), a spectacular landslip. The movement is due to water pressure in the massive, jointed RR lubricating the mobile shales beneath and was possibly initiated by springs at the Rowarth Fault. Notice the form of the slipped masses and the marshy ground down below. Slipped material overlies boulder clay, so it must post-date the glaciation, but pollen from the peaty hollows indicates disturbed ground from at least 5200

BC, therefore an age for the landslipping of between 10,000 and 7000 BP seems likely (Johnson, 1965). If time and agility permit, a walk 400m south along the edge to a stile and a careful scramble onto the rocks will reveal horizontal slickensides of one of the tear faults cutting the edge.

If the walk is to be terminated here, retrace the route to the quarries at Locality 6 and follow the fenced path northwards, past the triangulation point, to Monks' Road. Either follow the road back to the Grouse Inn, or for Glossop, cross the road, passing a new stone building, bear left round the plantation and head down past Hobroyd. Just past the entrance fork right, noting the position of the Charlestown borehole in the paddock on the left (this was a water bore at SK 02979331, which recorded 50' 8" drift, 62' 7" upper Kinderscout Grit, 87' 3" mudstones with Butterley Marine Band, 74' 6" lower Kinderscout Grit and 576' 6" of mudstones, siltstones and thin sandstones; see Stevenson & Gaunt, 1971). Cross the road and follow the flagged footpath over the footbridge and up to the A624, then turn left for the station which is 800m distant.

If continuing the walk, follow the path round the rim of Coombes and down the RR dip slope, which becomes Back Lane and runs down to the centre of Charlesworth, with shops and public houses.

Leave Charlesworth westwards down Long Lane. Just past the school the first of a number of roughly north-south trending faults is crossed. This one is the 10km long Rowarth Fault which downthrows up to 1 km to the west, so that we do not encounter RR again until the bottom of the hill. About half-way down the lane, by an isolated house on the right, notice that the valley we are approaching, the Etherow, proceeds in a series of narrow sections separated by wide parts; 'broad bottoms'. Notice the only remaining mill in the valley and beyond it the hill called Werneth Low. The pre-glacial course of the river Etherow took it through the col to the north of Werneth Low, but this is now filled with over 24m of glacial drift. Care must be exercised at the sharp bend in the road, and just before Besthill Bridge notice massive Rough Rock in an old quarry on the right (**Locality 8**, SJ 99659376, Figure 5b). This is the top of the RR. A similar looking RR appears across the river at the top of the cliff, though the beds forming the bulk of the cliff are the Rough Rock Flags (RRF), a local flaggy development of the lower part of the RR. The reason for the clear mismatch of beds across the river is the Viaduct Fault which runs NW-SE along the river here, downthrowing about 300m to the east.

Cross the river, and follow the road up to the railway bridge; turn right immediately past the bridge and follow the track on the right (Hague Road). In a short distance there is the dramatic view of Cat Tor (**Locality 9**, SJ 99529383), the sheer cliff of RR we saw from below at **Locality 8**. It is obvious that the

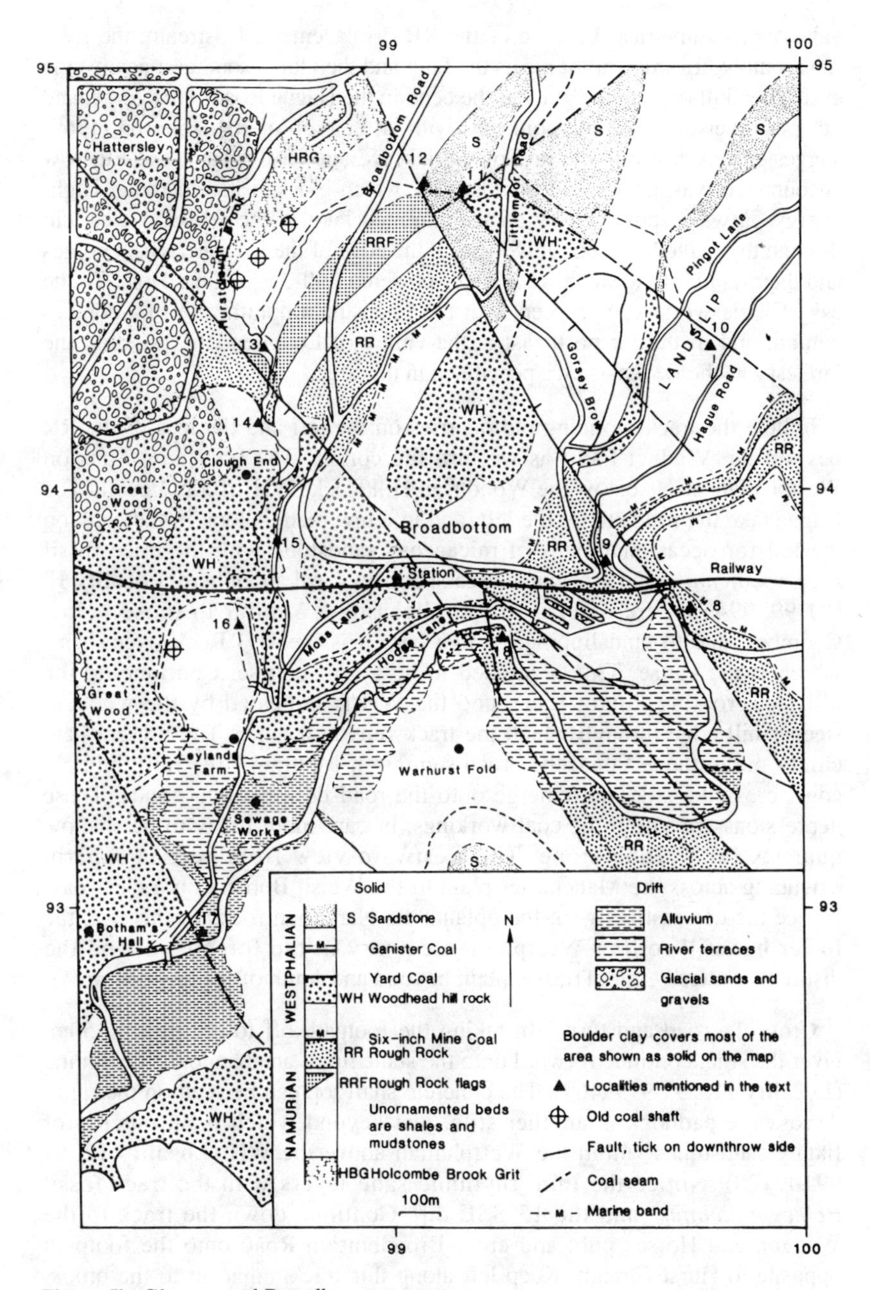

Figure 5b. Glossop and Broadbottom area.

valley is asymmetrical because of the RR displacement. Upstream, the river runs southwestwards until it meets the fault and then turns southeast against the cliff. The fault runs up the gully at the bend in the Hague Road. This gorge, and others further downstream, coincides with an outcrop of RR. Johnson (1969) suggested that towards the end of the last ice age (Devensian) the Etherow encountered wasting ice and boulder clay which blocked its old route. High-energy outwash, powered by an ice-dammed lake in the Glossop area, cut through the faulted RR, possibly beneath the edge of the ice sheet. Such gorges and their rapids are ideal sites for water-powered mills, as at Gnat Hole. To the east, Charlesworth can be seen with the imposing amphitheatre of Coombes behind, and in the far northeast is the valley of Longdendale, possibly the farthest east the Devensian ice penetrated in this area.

Follow the track, noticing old quarries on the left and the loss of the RR beyond the Viaduct Fault as we turn the corner. The track now runs on Westphalian shales below the Woodhead Hill Rock (WH). 100m beyond The Hague take the footpath on the left, and in a few metres, look in the bank on the left for occasional slabs of micaceous sandstone with the trace fossil *Pelecypodichnus* and associated escape burrows. All about here, **Locality 10** (SJ 99799435), are a series of parallel ridges similar to those below Coombes, due to landslipping, though here it is the WH Rock over shales which is the cause. This area used to be a golf course. Continue up the hillside, crossing Pingot Lane, and the WH is indicated by the wooded, steeper hill edge through which the track runs in a gully. The present path climbs out to the left onto the broad summit of Mottram Hill. Skirt the field edge, cross the stile and emerge onto the road between two ponds. These depressions are said to be coal workings, but are more likely to be shallow quarries for walling stone. The westward view from here is superb, extending across the Manchester plain to the Welsh Borders on a clear day. Notice the contrast between the uplands on Namurian rocks to the east, the lower but still rolling Westphalian country in the foregound, and the distinctly flatter Permo-Triassic plain beyond and south of the city centre.

Cross the road and turn left, taking the footpath off to the right in 50m. Over the stile, continue forward onto the shale tip of an abandoned coal mine (**Locality 11**, SJ 99199469). The concrete shaft top can be seen on the right. Across the paddock is another stile, just beyond which is an outcrop of flaggy sandstones within the Westphalian above the WH (**Locality 12**, SJ 99109470). Notice the thin, rhythmic sand layers with the trace fossil *Pelecypodichnus* and the 13°SSE dip. Continue down the track to the Waggon and Horses pub, and cross Broadbottom Road onto the footpath opposite to Hurst Clough. Keep left along this track, adjacent to the brook, and notice the skyline to the right; a broad plateau of glacial sand and gravel occupied by the Hattersley housing estate. The steep drop from the plateau to Hurst Clough is on Holcombe Brook Grit (=HWR). Old coal shafts and tips occur on the rough ground west of the track, but continue following the stream to its confluence with Hurstclough Brook. Here, the track is carried down over old tip material in steps. Notice the bright yellow-brown ochre (limonite) in the water emerging from an old mine drain (sough) and which colours the Hurstclough Brook for many metres downstream. Take the footbridge on the left, then immediately cross the brook to view a high river cliff of well-jointed micaceous siltstone below the Rough Rock Flags exhibiting spheroidal weathering (**Locality 13**, SJ 98709431).

Return to the track following the left bank of Hurstclough Brook downstream as it enters a narrow gorge in RRF. The steep sides of the gorge show evidence of severe soil creep, such as trees with curved lower trunks, as well as outcrops of RRF. Adjacent to the track is a tree, toppled by the movement of soil, which has continued growing and produced numerous new trunks from lateral branches. Where one track keeps to the contours to the left, the Hattersley Fault is crossed, but follow the steps alongside the stream and notice the water flowing over nearly south-dipping slabs of RR. The top of the Rough Rock occurs just downstream of a footbridge at the bottom of the steps (**Locality 14**, SJ 98699415) and is marked by the Six-inch Mine coal, which can be located as a line of dark material V-ing down to the stream among the trees on the far bank. A detour for a few metres over the footbridge shows this better near where the seam crosses an old trackway (gully). Another detour, 50m along the wide track to the east of the footbridge, reveals a quarry exposing 10m of partly shattered, massive RR, adjacent to the Hattersley Fault. Return to the clough and follow it downstream, over another footbridge onto the right bank, now noting the high, steep river cliff in 10°SE-dipping flaggy sandstones of WH forming the eastern side of the valley. Another footbridge returns the track to the left bank below this cliff, and as the track climbs to its highest point (**Locality 15**, SJ 98729385), look for evidence of coal working (black shale and coal pieces) of the Yard Coal at the top of the Woodhead Hill Rock to the left of the track.

On meeting the railway line, turn right and cross it by the footbridge. The footpath runs straight down the hill, following an outcrop of the Yard Coal which matches that previously seen on the opposite side of Hurst Clough. Amongst this hummocky ground (**Locality 16**, SJ 98649365) evidence of coal working and of mineral lines serving the pits can be found. Much of the land over to the right, adjacent to the railway, is tipped glacial sand and gravel excavated from a deep railway cutting just out of sight to the west. The railway previously ran in a tunnel here, but the overburden was removed and dumped, then the masonry tunnel lining was demolished by shunting empty waggons inside and then blowing up the tunnel, after which the wagons were hauled away, and rail services resumed! Go through the kissing gate, and follow the steps, turning left at the first junction by the bungalow called Oakenash. At the stream do not cross the footbridge but turn right down to the hamlet of Hodgefold.

If time and energy are wanting, it is recommended that **Locality 17** (this paragraph) is omitted and the signed path following the Etherow is followed eastwards (left, next paragraph). Otherwise, from Hodgefold, follow the fenced track (Leylands Lane) south, through the gate at Leylands Farm (SJ 98649340) and past the sewage works by the River Etherow on the left. Notice on the right the abandoned meander on the river terrace; behind the terrace the land rises to Great Wood. This rolling landscape is underlain by a great thickness of glacial sand and gravel, and forms a broad col between Mottram Hill and Werneth Low (the hill dominating the skyline to the southwest). Before the last glaciation, the Etherow flowed west towards Manchester between these two hills, but after the glaciation the river was forced to change its course to flow southwards because of the sand, gravel and ice blocking the old route to the west. Continue down the track until a footpath is seen crossing a small meadow on the left. Cross the stile and follow the path to the banks of the river. Here, at 'Broadbottom Beach' (**Locality 17**, SJ 98539293, once a popular bathing spot), the river pebbles may be searched fruitfully for erratics, examples of imbrication and other sedimentary features. The river cliff opposite shows glacial sand and gravel. The exposure in the river cliff on the right bank a few hundred metres downstream (below Botham's Hall) may be viewed by returning to the lane, crossing the bridge, and following the river bank to the first bend, but it may be overgrown. Here, the tripartite divisions of Upper Boulder Clay (0.6-0.9m), Middle Sands (12.5m), and Lower Boulder Clay (1.0-1.3m) were recorded by Johnson (1969). Analyses of the two boulder clays revealed that they are indistinguishable and, therefore, the sand and gravel between were probably deposited during a period of ice stagnation, rather than during an interglacial. Return by the same route to Hodgefold and keep right along the path (Hodge Lane) which follows the river.

About 100m east of Hodgefold there is a small lodge on the left which once fed Hodge Dye Works (SJ 98919350), seen on the right. The dye works has been excavated recently, and shows very large flags of beautifully rippled sandstone. No flags of this kind are encountered on this excursion, but they resemble the Namurian Haslingden Flags which are approximately equivalent to the Rough Rock Flags and are widely used as walling slabs throughout the region. They must have been brought here from north of Manchester by canal most of the way. 200m along the path on the left is Summerbottom, a row of weavers cottages. The lower two floors were living accommodation and bridges from the steep bank behind give access to work space in the garrets under the eaves. Follow the roughly cobbled lane further and in 100m Lee Bangs Rocks are reached. This is Rough Rock, considerably lower than at Cat Tor, indicating a fault between the two localities downthrowing to the west. It also indicates that we have crossed the Hattersley Fault (which downthrows to the west) and are back onto Namurian rocks. Follow the path down to the footbridge, which takes advantage of the extremely narrow gorge, cut sub-glacially in the RR (**Locality 18**, SJ 99289365). On the far side of the bridge is an outcrop of massive grit, showing large, rotten concretions at the bases of the beds. The river here flows rapidly and there is more evidence of old mills on the banks.

Recross the bridge and turn right (Old Street), then left up the steep Mill Brow and under the railway bridge. This emerges onto the main road; Broadbottom station, the terminus of the walk, is 350m to the left.

ITINERARY V

Goyts Moss and Burbage, Derbyshire

R. M. C. Eagar

Ordnance Survey 1:50,000 Sheet 119
British Geological Survey 1:50,000 Sheet 111; 1:25,000 SK07

This itinerary provides opportunities to study well exposed basal Westphalian strata in a small, long abandoned coalfield at the head of the Goyt Valley and to collect excellently preserved non-marine 'mussels'. Emphasis has been placed on the rich faunal succession above the Bassy Mine (Goyts Coal) and above the horizon of the Lower Foot Mine (Eagar, 1952, 1956). Both these faunal successions, formerly finely exposed in quarries west of Wigan (Eagar, *in* Broadhurst *et al.*, 1970), may now be seen only in part in the area west of Wigan (Eagar, *in* Bathurst, *et al.*, 1965).

The itinerary commences at Christ Church (SK 044729) Burbage, reached by buses from Buxton, and finishes at the same point. The walking distance is about 8km over hilly moorland country and the trip is best undertaken in the summer months. Details of the area shown in Figure 6, however, may be

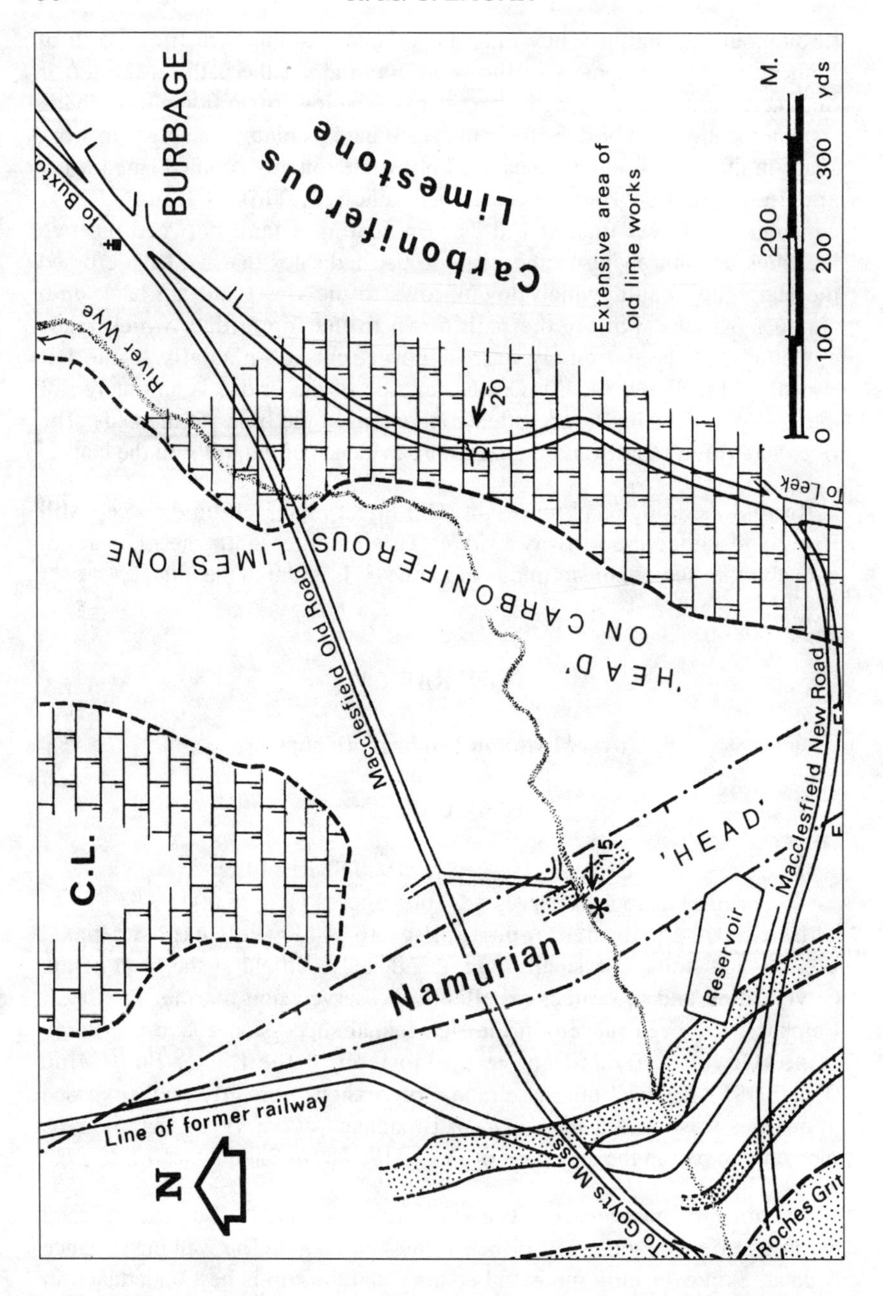

Figure 6. Sketch-map of the area southwest of Burbage.

studied at any time. Motorists can reach the central Goyts Moss sections from the Buxton-Macclesfield New Road (A537) by turning north at SK 020710 ("Derbyshire Bridge only") and approaching them from the south. It should be noted that cars must not leave the Goyts Moss car park (Figure 7, centre, right) by going northwards down the Goyt Valley; the road is one-way (southwards) only. Cars can also be parked along the side of the Buxton-Macclesfield Old Road just beyond its surfacing limit (SK 035724, Figure 6, west of the crossing faults).

Route. From Burbage Church follow the road southwestwards taking the right fork down Macclesfield Old Road. After crossing the River Wye (SK 041727) note the much weathered and greatly overgrown outcrops and quarried sections of upper Viséan limestones immediately north of the road and in the distance east of the Macclesfield New Road, where there was formerly much quarrying between Burbage and Ladmanlow. These rocks have yielded Asbian fossils. Turn left down Level Lane and, at the end of the straight road, continue on the narrow signposted public footpath, turning sharply right in 20 metres to go over a stile (SK 038724) and follow the stream bank, skirting private property to the right. A section of shales steeply dipping west is well exposed 20m upstream (SK 03707235) from a crossing pipe. Shales with sulphurous weathering lying about 0.3 to 1.9m below the highest exposed beds yield abundant goniatites, including *Reticuloceras bilingue*. The bivalve *Dunbarella* may be found lower down. The section exposes beds above a sandstone seen in the stream, which is much brown stained by water rich in iron carbonate. Cope (1965) traced the sandstone northwards on to limestones of Asbian or low Brigantian age, indicating an apparent overlap within the Namurian and an overstep of the upper Namurian onto the limestones, but later work by the Geological Survey has yielded a very different interpretation of the solid geology (Figure 6). There is comparatively little evidence on the ground largely because of blanketing by 'head'. This is a periglacial deposit of clay, sandy clay and sandy loam with many sandstone fragments of all sizes, the result of solifluction, a process of alternate freezing and thawing, during the Pleistocene epoch. From evidence partly outside the area of Figure 6, it is very likely that the goniatite band is separated from the limestone outcrop by a fault.

The general sequence of the upper part of the Namurian and of the basal Westphalian south and west of Buxton may be summarised as follows:

TABLE 3
Uppermost Namurian and lowest Westphalian successions in Goyts Trough and the central Pennines

Goyts Trough Area	Pennine Equivalents
Honley Marine Band (=Lower Foot Mine M.B. of Buxton Geol. Surv. Mem. 1985)	Honley Marine Band
Non-Marine beds, *Carbonicola obliqua* maximum	*C. obliqua* maximum in West Lancs.
Coal and seat-earth absent	Middle Band Coal — Lower Foot Mine
Sedimentary cycle not distinguishable from cycle below.	Upper Division of shell succession above the Soft Bed — Bassy Mine Succession
Marine band absent	Springwood (=Upper-Bassy) Marine Band
Middle Division of Soft Bed —Bassy Mine Succession	Middle Division of Soft Bed — Bassy Mine Succession
Holbrook Marine Band — *Lingula* with rare *Gastrioceras* sp.	Holbrook (=Lower Bassey) Marine Band — *Lingula* and occasionally *Orbiculoidea*
Lower Division of the Soft Bed —Bassy Mine Succession.	Lower Division of the Soft Bed —Bassy Mine Succession.
Yard, or Goyts Coal	Yard or Soft Bed-Bassy Mine Succession
c. 30m WOODHEAD HILL ROCK	
c. 18m of shales	Shales
Gastrioceras subcrenatum Marine Band (Base of Westphalian)	
Poorly developed coal horizon	Pot Clay Coal — Six Inch Mine
c. 30m ROUGH ROCK	
c. 65m of shales and mudstones	Upper Haslingden Flags
Gastrioceras cumbriense Marine Band	
4m of shale	Lower Haslingden Flags
Gastrioceras cancellatum Marine Band	
Simmondley Coal, up to 8m above Ringinglow Coal	Holcombe Brook Coal
CHATSWORTH GRIT *c.* 30m (HUDDERSFIELD WHITE ROCK)	HOLCOMBE BROOK GRIT
Shales, mudstones and thin grits c. 28m	Shales, mudstones, flags and grits with a marine band and thin coal
Reticuloceras superbilingue Marine Band	
Thin coal and seat-earth	Thin local coal or seat-earth
ROACHES GRIT, with upper leaf of *c.* 45m and three variably developed lower leaves extending through *c.* 95m	GUISELEY GRIT or HAZEL GREAVE GRIT
CORBAR GRIT (to the north), c. 60m	Reticuloceras bilingue (late) M.B.
c. 145m of shales and mudstones	PULE HILL GRIT and shales below it
Reticuloceras bilingue Marine Band	

Return to the Macclesfield Old Road via the footpath northwest of the reservoir, turning sharply right to reach the Macclesfield Old Road above the tunnel entrance of the old railway (SK 035723). Note the outcrops of Roaches Grit, dipping westwards, further along the road. The Chatsworth Grit, with underlying mudstones, is well exposed in the bank of a small stream just north of the road (SK 030722), and may be seen to form a prominent feature, as do other grits in this area as they dip into the Goyt Syncline. At the highest point on the Macclesfield Old Road (SK 027722) the Rough Rock crops out in the road and shows cross-bedding, the foresets indicating derivation of the material from the southwest. Follow the road westwards down the dip slope into the depression of Barry Clough, where the stream to the north of the road exposes mudstones between the Rough Rock and the Woodhead Hill Rock. The latter forms the next rise in the road and may be seen in a small quarry 100m to the south (SK 025719) and just beyond the eastern limit of Figure 7, where the grit dips westward towards the axis of the Goyt Syncline. Continue down the road, noting the flattening out of higher beds around **Localities 7** and **8** of Figure 7. Thence walk westwards and look for the Woodhead Hill Rock on the western limb of the syncline. Its top, consisting of ganisteroid sandstone, is well exposed in the bed of the River Goyt, south and west of **Locality 1**, where roots and rootlets are seen extending down through about one metre of seatearth. The overlying seam, known locally at Goyts Coal, consists of about 1.5m of mainly bright coal with numerous bands of dark carbonaceous shale rich in plant debris and is usually well exposed at **Locality 4**. Although of poor quality this seam was formerly much mined for lime-burning at a time when difficulties of transport weighed against the importation of better quality coal (see Robert & Leach, 1985). Note the abundant evidence of old workings, which were usually bell pits (Figure 7).

The faunal succession above the horizon of the Soft Bed — Bassy Mine shows a remarkable uniformity over almost all of the Pennine area. It consists of three upwardly coarsening sedimentary cycles (or divisions) rich in non-marine bivalve faunas separated by two thin marine bands (Eagar, 1947, 1952, 1956). At Goyts Moss the Lower and Middle Divisions are seen clearly but the Upper Division cannot be recognised and appears to be absent. The Lower Division, of dark shales and shaly mudstones grading up through shaly to lighter coloured silty mudstones, may be examined at **Locality 1** (SK 017716; see the lettered left-hand section of the inset to Figure 7). Fish scales and debris are abundant from 23 to 90cm above the coal. The fauna of Band C includes thin shelly layers with all sizes of the morphological species *Carbonicola fallax*, *C. rectilinearis* and *C. pilleolum*, which are characterised by an oblique carinal (ridge-like) swelling running

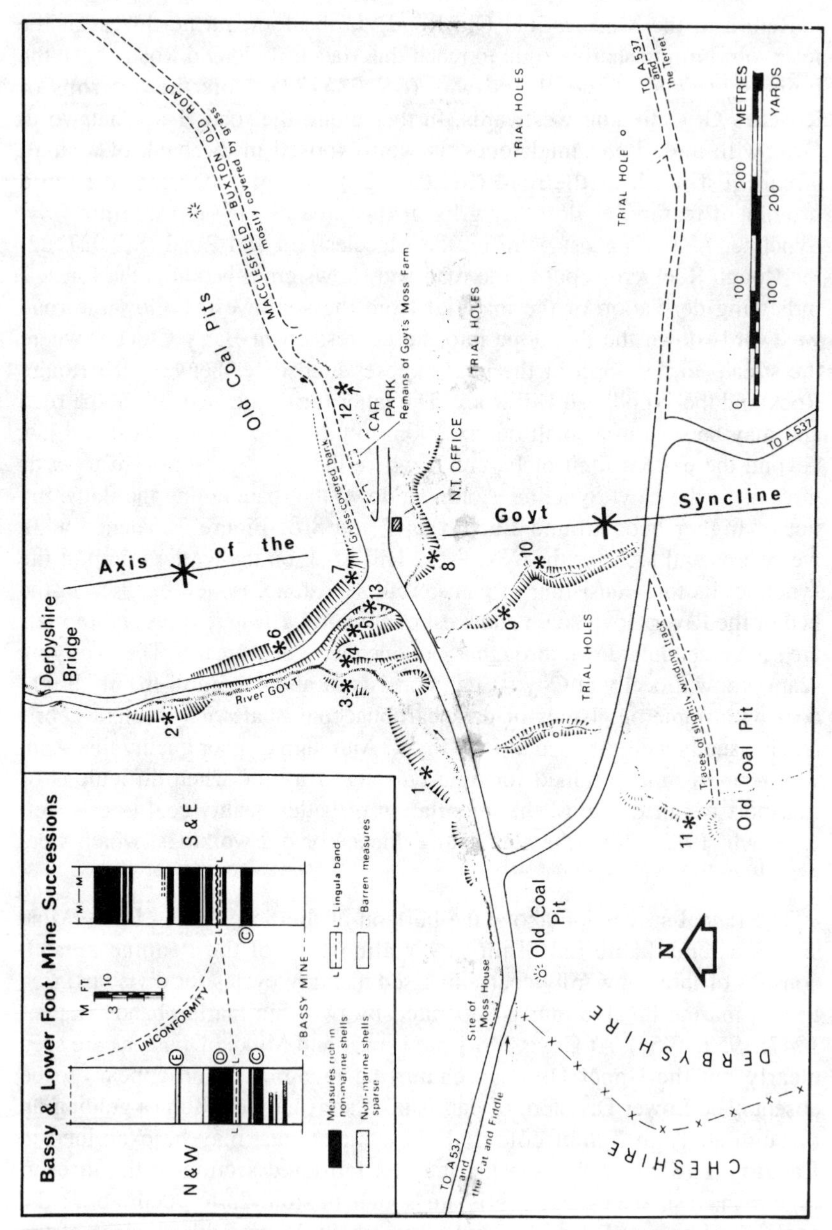

Figure 7. Sketch-map of Goyts Moss area. Asterisks denote sections referred to in the text. The sections shown inset form part of a series of continuous exposures between the sections marked 1, 2, 5, 13, 7, 12, 10, and 11.

from the umbo towards the posterior angle of the shell. There are also thin layers of *Curvirimula* sp. especially towards the base of the band. These features are typical of the Lower Division over the whole Pennine area (Eagar 1947, figure 8). The silty grey mudstones are unusual however in that their fauna of *Carbonicola protea* also yields varieties trending towards *C. discus*, a subcircular trend unknown elsewhere on this horizon. The overlying band of *Lingula* with abundant fish scales and rare *Gastrioceras* is *c.* 6mm in thickness. It lies 3.65 to c. 4.6m above the coal and may be traced eastwards easily by the presence of a 15cm band of feruginous coarse-grained silty mudstone which lies c. 18cm below it. The beds of the Lower Division expand slightly when traced eastward to **Localities 3, 4** and **5**, and their lower parts become less fossiliferous. (Figure 7, inset, right-hand section, bottom). The *Lingula* band can be traced to a section below the level of the road, Locality 13, just north of stepped shoring blocks on the bank of the stream.

The Middle Division is well exposed at **Locality 2** (SK 017718) and in the beds immediately above the Goyt and below the road between **Localities 2** and **6**, preservation being particularly good in the latter section where 'solid' material is readily obtainable from carbonate nodules. Band D (of Figure 7, inset) yields small elongate *Carbonicola* including *Anthraconaia*-like varieties, *Carbonicola* aff. *artifex* and *C. cf. limax* in fine-grained carbonaceous shales. Within the same very abundant series of the thin layers there also occurs, particularly in the middle and upper parts, varieties of elongate oval *Carbonicola*, including *C.* aff. *protea*, such as are characteristic of the lower and middle parts of the Middle Division. Band E is marked by a slight decrease in grain size and an increase in the carbonaceous and pyritous content of the sediment. It is noticeable for the occurrence of *Curvirimula, Spirorbis* and fish scales. This sedimentary and faunal change is typical of the *Carbonicola discus* band in the Middle Division elsewhere (Eagar 1952, 1956 pl. xxvii), although *Carbonicola discus* has not been found at Goyts Moss. The section however is virtually identical to that found at Pott Shrigley, 10km to the north of Goyts Moss (*ibid.*, pl. xxvii, section V, where *C. discus* is present, so that the *discus* horizon is not in any doubt).

The sections at **Locality 2**, and further south (see p. 44) indicate a progressive upward coarsening of grain size above the *discus* horizon and thus there appears to be no representation of the Springwood or Upper Bassy Mine Marine Band; nor is there any sedimentological separation of a representative of the Upper Division in the remainder of the exposed succession.

On the east bank of the road, about 60m south of the southern limit of the exposure marked **Locality 2**, (SK 017717) a small fault may be seen, its plane obscured but with a downthrow to the south of just over 2m. 5 to 15m further south of the fault, at **Locality 6**, a hard, fine-grained sandstone, 30 to 50cm thick merges northwards with similar sandstone about 10.5m above the coal, but southwards cuts down progressively into finer-grained siltstones and mudstones below it. By temporarily clearing scree from the lower part of the bank the disconformable relationship can be traced to just over 25 m south of the fault, as was first observed by Cope (1949). In the early part of the 1950s it was possible to see the sandstone lying on progressively lower horizons southward in the sections exposed between the road and the River Goyt, but the bank was later shored up and the intermediate sections covered over, so that only one now remains. The latter is 20 to 25m north of the bridge and immediately north of a series of of stepped shoring blocks (Figure 7, **Locality 13**) below the railings of the road. At this point the unconformable sandstone, 18cm thick, lies only 23cm above the Lingula (Holbrook) Marine Band. Thus between Localities 6 and 13 about 8 or 9m of the succession in the north of the Goyts Moss area have been removed by erosion, as indicated in the inset sketch of Figure 7. In several places the erosional surface has been scoured by burrowing, as may be seen by inspection of the undersurface of the unconformable thin sandstone. This bears infillings of the burrows, the trace fossil *Rhizocorallium* cf. *R. jenense*, originally found by Hardy (1970) and described by Eagar *et al* (1985, pl. 14A-E). These burrows, which appear typically as small striated crescent shapes with diameters of 2 to 3cm, may have been made by a temporary incursion of small marine animals into a scoured channel, but the precise nature of the animals is as yet unknown. It is particularly requested that blocks of the sandstone be left *in situ*.

Mudstones succeeding the thin sandstone contain numerous bands of non-marine bivalves in two main groups, A and B of the inset sketch. These sediments are lithologically and palaeontologically distinct from those in the succession above the Goyts Coal, though have not been differentiated by the Geological Survey (Aitkenhead, *et al.* 1985, p. 95 and figure 35, where these bands are omitted). The mudstones are richly pyritous, with pyrite blebs especially common in the lowest metre and the highest exposed 60cm below the Honley (Lower Foot) Marine Band. Preservation occurs commonly as pyritic replacement of the shells. Small forms under a length of 2cm can be found uncrushed, so that exquisite material, with both valves in closed position, can be obtained. The shells are distributed in moderate numbers in thin layers so time and patience are needed in collection, since casual inspection may fail to reveal any shells. Shells have been found as far south as in **Locality 11**, but to the author's knowledge the best material has been found in **Localities 8, 9** and **10**.

The fauna consists of three groups of biospecies of *Carbonicola* and less commonly very small shells of *Curvirimula*. Communities of large *Carbonicola obliqua* are dominant with varieties trending to oval forms (Eagar, 1956, figure 50-w). Slightly smaller oval to wedge-shaped shells are referable to *C*.cf. *bipennis* (*ibid*., a-e; pl. xxvi, figure viii). These decrease in numbers upward in the succession and become uncommon at the top. Communities of the small *Carbonicola artifex (ibid*., pl. xxvi, figure iii) occur intermittently throughout in moderate numbers, being more common in Band A than Band B. Variation in this latter group extends to shells very near *C. fallax* (*ibid*., figure iv) but differing from this species in being smaller, with more nearly oval form in lateral view and with a broader carinal swelling than is found in the *C. fallax* faunas of the Lower Division of the Bassy Mine succession.

The shells of Bands A and B belong unquestionably to the faunas dominantly of *Carbonicola obliqua* which are well known above the horizon of the Lower Foot Mine in Lancashire (Eagar, 1956) and compare closely with those on this horizon, and immediately below the Honley (Lower Foot) Marine Band at Ravenhead Brickworks, Up Holland. The latter may be seen at **Locality 12** at Goyts Moss (SK 01907157), at a small waterfall just north of the car park. The section includes two thin *Lingula* leaves:

Rather soft weathered grey and black shales	0.43m
Medium to light grey shelly mudstone, much jointed and ironstained, with a thin course of *Lingula* and fish scales 2.5 cm from the top	7.6cm
Hard, blue-black to grey, mainly ironstained shale with *Posidonia gibsoni*, *Caneyella* and less commonly, poorly preserved *Gastrioceras*	8.2cm
Dark sulphurous weathering shale with *Lingula*	2.5cm
Contorted dark slickensided shale	2-15cm
Grey, fine-grained shaly mudstone, slightly more coarse-grained towards the base	25.5cm
Hard gritty mudstone	18.0cm

The marine band can also be exposed by digging into the top of the bank above the section of **Locality 8.**

Similarity of the Goyts Moss and Up Holland sequences extends also below the horizon of the *Carbonicola obliqua* beds. At Ravenhead Brickworks (SJ 512048) a sandstone nearly 4m below the beds lies without obvious disconformity on siltstones of the upper part of the Upper Division of the Bassy Mine succession. The sandstone, varying from 0.3 to 5m in thickness, descends to cut out about 8m of the Upper Division beds within 0.8km to the southeast of the brickworks (Eagar, 1951; Eagar, *in* Broadhurst *et al.* 1970, pp.22-4). Moreover, these two unconformable sandstones both reveal the very unusual trace fossil *Rhizocorallium* cf. *R. jenense* at the bases (Eagar, *et al.* 1985, p.126). Therefore it is likely that the two erosional events were comtemporaneous, or nearly so. They may well indicate channelling into earlier deposited beds during the formation of the coal of the Lower Foot Mine.

Follow the road northward down the Goyt Valley. At 25m south of Derbyshire Bridge a steep clough on the east bank of the Goyt shows Goyts Coal, its ganister and seatearth finely exposed at the bottom above the Woodhead Hill Rock. The sequence above the coal reveals the Lower and Middle Divisions of the Bassy Mine succession, the latter passing upwards into sandstone without trace of the Lower Foot Mine succession. Further south down the road the river cuts down into the sandstone notably at the confluence of an eastern tributary (SK 018721), exposing good examples of cross-bedding, mostly suggesting from the dips a southerly source for the sediment. Further downstream (SK 017723) the river reaches the base of the Woodhead Hill Rock, which can be traced readily by a line of springs at its junction with underlying impervious mudstones. Note the greener vegetation just below the springs.

The Itinerary may be completed by walking down to the confluence of the Goyt and Berry Clough and taking the signposted footpath to Buxton, across the Goyt by a footbridge and thence up the valley to meet the Macclesfield Old Road.

ITINERARY VI

Low Side Brickworks, Glodwick and Rocher Vale, Park Bridge, near Oldham

F. M. Broadhurst

Ordnance Survey 1:50,000 Sheet 109; 1:25,000 SD 80/90
British Geological Survey 1:50,000 Sheet 85

This excursion can be made on foot, starting and finishing at the disused Lowside Brickworks (SD 942041) Glodwick, near Oldham centre. The walking distance is about 5km along fairly easy paths or roadways. The excursion can also be done by private transport, parking space being available near the brickworks quarry and at the Park Bridge Visitor Centre. The rocks to be seen belong to Westphalian A and B. Further details about the geology are to be found in Tonks *et al*, 1931.

Route: The excursion begins at the disused Lowside Brickworks quarry (SD 942041), Glodwick, Oldham (Figures 8 & 9, **Locality 1**). Parking is available for several cars/minibuses in a lay-by behind a chapel on Roundthorn Road (SD 943042). The succession in the quarry face is of Westphalian A age.

The lowest stratigraphic exposures (Figure 9, A) are towards the southeastern end of the quarry. Here a succession of thin sandstones is seen to alternate with thin siltstones. The sandstones reveal load structures, where masses of sand have sunk downwards into underlying silts.The development of the sands as thin sheets suggests that they were formed as successive splays, each representing deposition from flood waters supplied from an adjacent river channel via overbank flooding or through fissured levées (crevasses). This sequence is interrupted in places by erosion channels occupied by sandstone fills. Towards the top of this sandstone/siltstone succession rootlets become apparent, but they need to be searched for carefully on account of the weathering that has taken place since the quarry was worked. These rootlets were associated with the Oldham Great Seam (correlated with the Trencherbone Seam elsewhere in the Lancashire Coalfield) which formerly lay above but has long since been removed. The former position of the Oldham Great Seam is indicated on Figure 9. Walk up the ramp of the former inclined railway to a point where a low cliff of carbonaceous clayrocks becomes easily accessible (Figure 9, B). This cliff contains bands and concretions of clay ironstone (siderite-cemented clay), which weather to produce brown-red colouration. These rocks also contain

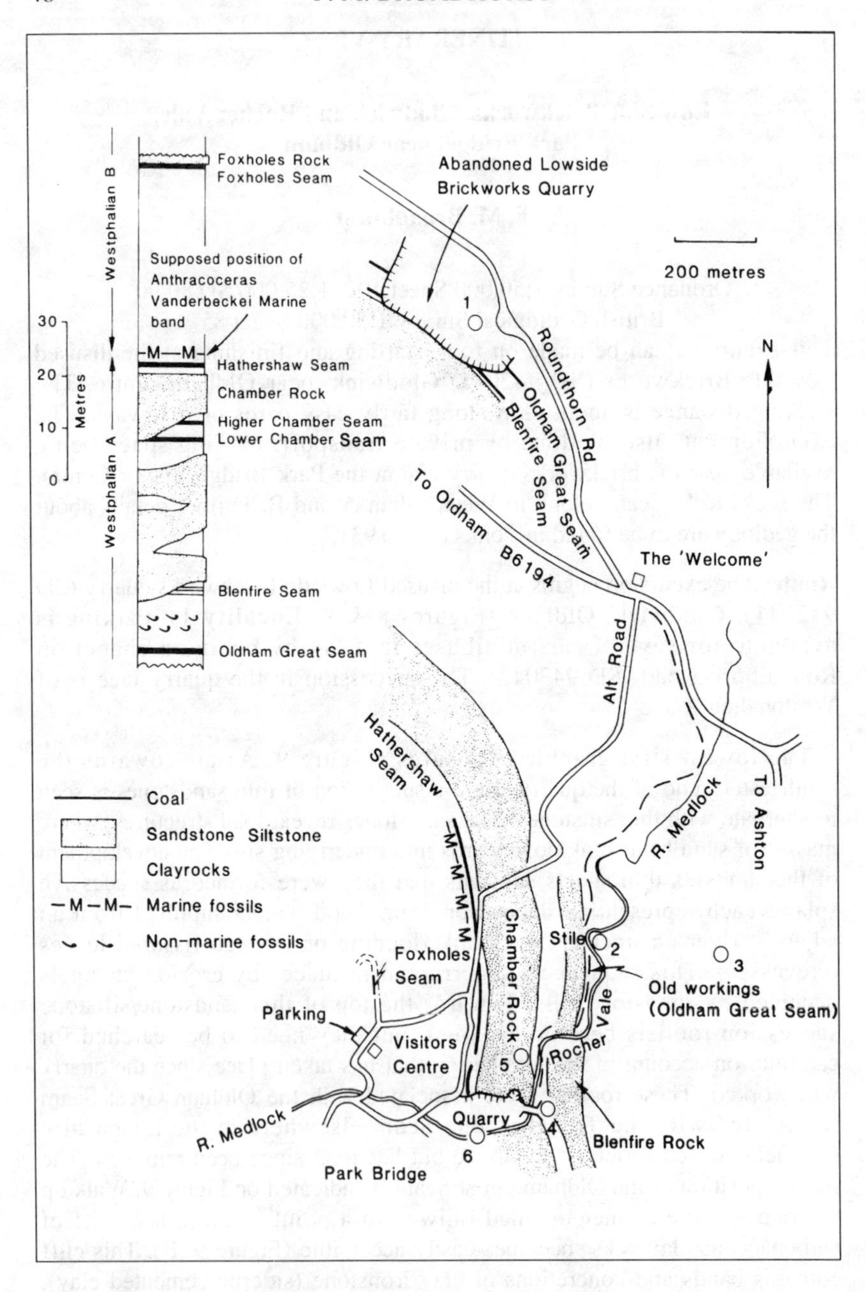

Figure 8. Sketch-map of Rocher Vale and Park Bridge area.

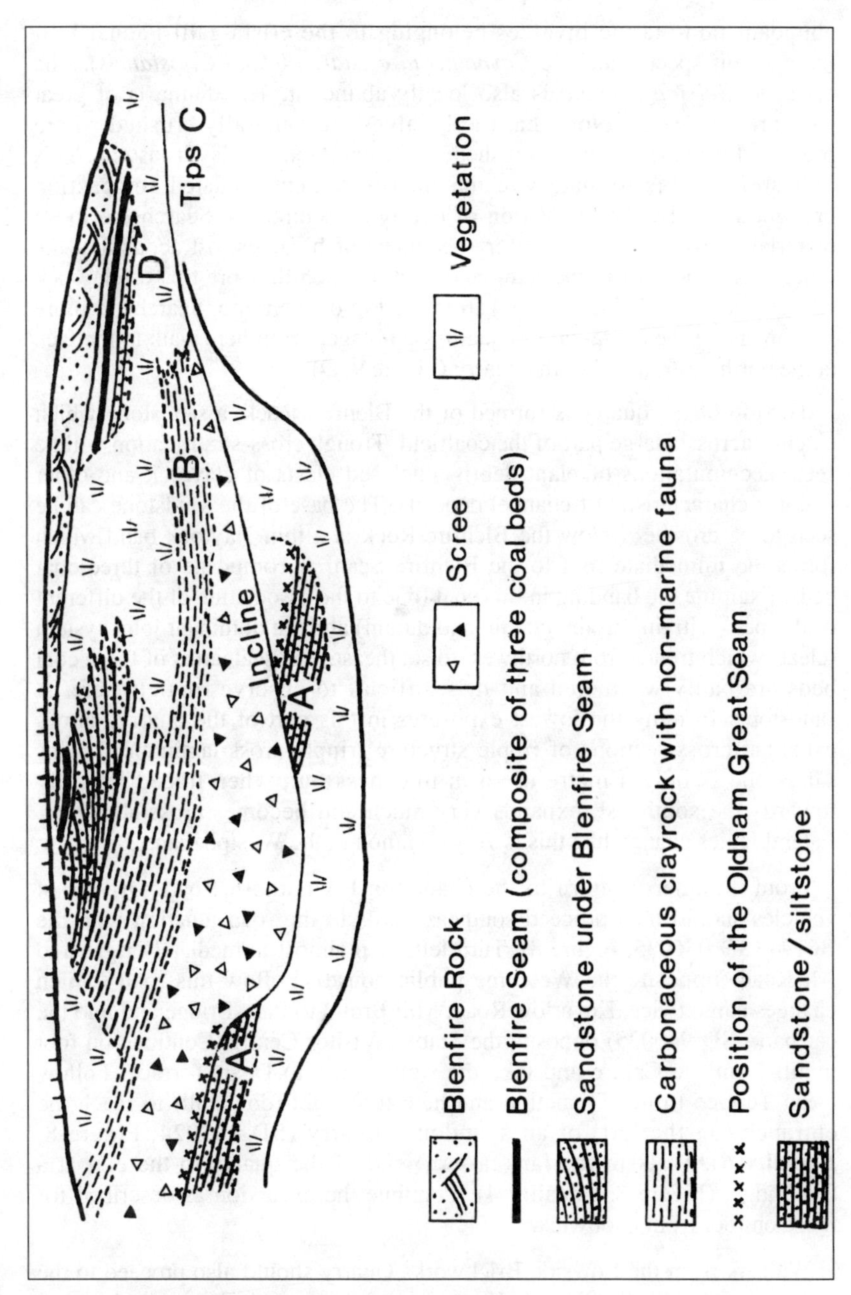

Figure 9. Low side Brickworks quarry, viewed from the north.

abundant non-marine bivalves belonging to the crista-galli Faunal Belt (component species include *Carbonicola crista-galli and C. oslancis*). The ostracod *Geisina arcuata* is also locally abundant. This fauna is of great stratigraphic value. Note that the bivalves are generally crushed where preserved in clayrock but uncrushed where enclosed by clay ironstone. This indicates that the formation of the siderite cement predated compaction brought about by the deposition of overlying sediments. Search the loose material below the cliff face for specimens of bivalves, ostracods and the other fossils. Return to the ramp and continue uphill. More tips of clayrock will be seen ahead (Figure 9, C) from the top of the ramp. Search for more specimens of the crista-galli Faunal Assemblage. From here walk to the face at the northwestern end of the quarry (Figure 9, D).

The top of the quarry is formed of the Blenfire Rock, a sandstone which extends across a large part of the coalfield. Trough cross-stratification will be seen, accumulations of plant debris, enclosed clasts of clayrock and other features characteristic of channel deposits. The base of the sandstone can be seen to be erosive. Below the Blenfire Rock is a thin clayrock band which forms the immediate roof to the Blenfire Seam, a composite of three coal beds. Examine the banding in this coal (due to the association of the different coal types - vitrain, fusain, clarain and durain) and the dominant joint system (cleat) which trends from northwest to southeast. The seatearths of these coal beds are badly weathered and it is difficult to observe rootlets here. A sandstone, forming the lowest exposures in this part of the quarry, shows excellent cross-sections of ripple structure (ripple cross-lamination). This sandstone is only a metre or so in thickness but, when traced laterally towards the southeast, expands very much and becomes cross-stratified. Lateral facies change like this is very common in the Westphalian.

From the quarry return to the chapel on Roundthorn Road. Drivers of vehicles should then proceed southeastwards to the road junction with the B6194 (SD 946035, Figure 8). Turn left, then almost immediately right into Alt Road (opposite the Welcome public house). Follow this road (which changes name twice, Keverlow Road, Mill Brow) to Park Bridge and into the car park (SD 940025) opposite the Stables Visitor Centre. Continue on foot uphill from the Centre and take the right turn into Dean Terrace. Follow Dean Terrace to the T-junction and here turn right (downhill) to reach the entrance (on the left) of an abandoned quarry (SD 943024, Figure 8, **Locality 6**). Walk to the far (eastern) end of the quarry to the exit at a footbridge, (Figure 8, **Locality 4**). Continue the excursion as described for those on foot from Glodwick.

Walkers from the Lowside Brickworks Quarry should also proceed to the road junction with the B6194. Here turn left (eastwards), pass the junction with Alt Road, and after walking about 300 m turn off through a stile to the right. The pathway leads down to the River Medlock, passes alongside disused filter beds then bears away from the river. The route continues in a downstream direction but at some distance from the river, to avoid meanders. The route is marked by low posts with green arrows. The valley is wide at first but narrows into a gorge (Rocher Vale, entry to which is marked by a stile (SD 945027, Figure 8, **Locality 2**). Note the terracettes ("sheep tracks"), particularly well developed on the opposite bank of the stream. Terracettes result from downhill soil creep. Beyond the stile and into the gorge extensive exposures of carbonaceous clayrocks and siltrocks, on the opposite bank, show well the westerly dip. Alongside the path (SD 945026, Figure 8, **Locality 3**) there is evidence of coal workings (Oldham Great Seam) and in the bank above the path sandstones and siltstones represent the Blenfire Rock. These beds are better seen after a right hand bend in the Medlock brings them down to stream level. The channel facies seen in the Blenfire Rock at the brickworks quarry is here replaced by generally finer-grained sediments lacking clayrock clasts, etc. This is another example of a lateral facies change in the Westphalian.

Beyond the weir the Medlock takes another bend, this time to the left. The bank (SD 943024) above the path exposes a thick sandstone, the Chamber Rock (**Locality 5**). Continue to the footbridge, formerly a railway bridge (Figure 8, **Locality 4**) and to the quarry entrance with exposures of the Chamber Rock. The base of this sandstone rests on an erosion surface which is well seen above the river at Locality 4 of Figure 8. Elsewhere this erosion surface cuts out the Higher and Lower Chamber Seams, respectively.

The succession exposed in the quarry, (Figure 8, **Locality 6**) is about 40m thick. At the quarry entrance, adjacent to the bridge, a sequence of sandstones about 3m thick, with cross-stratification and parallel bedding is succeeded by 2 metres of siltstones and fine sandstone in which much brecciation and distortion is apparent, suggesting that this bed has accommodated lateral movement at some time. Above this brecciated horizon are thin sandstones (splay sheets?) containing various clasts, notably of clay ironstone.

The main quarry face, used by rock climbers, is of a medium grain-sized sandstone, at least 10m thick, trough cross-stratification indicating deposition in the form of arcuate-crested sand waves. These deposits probably accumulated on a river channel floor. The succession above the sandstone shows an overall change towards the development of fine-grained sandstones then siltstones, that is, the sequence is generally fining-up. The sandstones exhibit superb ripple structures in cross-section, including climbing ripples.

Erosion channels are numerous, themselves often filled with fining-up sequences. The high energy environment represented by the trough cross-stratified sandstone was apparently progressively replaced by quieter environments, possibly as a result of an important channel being 'switched' to some other location, as frequently happens in modern deltaic environments.

From the quarry continue (westwards) to Mill Brow (SD 942024) turn left past the Post Office and continue until an acute right turn is reached. Take the right turn, cross the River Medlock and walk up to the Stables Visitor Centre (exhibits on industrial history, natural history, warden service, refreshments). Enter the car park opposite the centre to examine the paving flags and setts which are mostly made of sandstone. There is, however, one sett made of Shap Granite.

Continue uphill, to Dingle Terrace, at the far end of which (SD 939026) is a stile leading to a roadway in a rock cutting. Here, there is an exposure of carbonaceous clayrocks and associated coal bands, collectively the Foxholes Seam, together with lighter seatearths (note the rootlets). The cleat in the coal again trends from northwest to southeast. This seam overlies the position of the Anthracoceras vanderbeckei Marine Band, so is Westphalian B in age.

The return journey for walkers involves walking back along Dingle Terrace, then turning left, eastwards (Figure 8) along Dean Terrace to join Keverlow Lane and Alt Lane back to the 'Welcome' and on towards Oldham.

ITINERARY VII

Jumbles Country Park, Bolton

K. Riley

Ordnance Survey 1:50,000 Sheet 109; 1:25,000 SD 61/71
British Geological Survey 1:63,360 Sheet 76; 1:50,000 Sheet 85

The purpose of this itinerary, which can extend to a half or full day, is to visit typical sections in the Namurian and Westphalian strata of the Silesian (Upper Carboniferous) north of Bolton. Walkers may start and finish at Bromley Cross Station, reached from Manchester Victoria (on Mondays to Fridays only). All the exposures are adjacent to roads, and parking places are shown in Figure 10. Drivers of vehicles should take the A676 from Bolton due north for approximately 3km. At the traffic lights (SD 733119) turn left into Turton Road (B6391) and in 1km turn right into Chapeltown Road, signposted Turton. In 200m Bromley Cross Station is reached, where there is a large open-access car park. Alternatively **Localities 1,2,5** and **3** with **4** can be driven to directly.

Route. From Bromley Cross Station walk south down Chapeltown Road to its junction with Turton Road (Figure 10). Turn left and in approximately 1km turn left again at the traffic lights (SD 7333120) towards Bradshaw Brow. Note that some of the cottages on the north side of the road still have the original sandstone flags on the roof, while others now have Welsh Slates (re-roofed since the railway came to Bolton). Take the track on the south side of the road, between the Stable (a Girl Guide hut) and the Royal Oak to the far side of the football pitch (SD 734119), from which exposures of a sandstone (Westphalian A) can be seen on the far side of Bradshaw Brook. Cross over the wooden bridge, adjacent to which about 4 metres of sandstone overlies about half a metre of poorly exposed dark blue micaceous shale which has yielded non-marine bivalves (**Locality 1**). Erosion surfaces and channels are well developed in the sandstone as are sandstone concretions (patches of sand which have been cemented with ferroan calcite, now weathered by acid rain). An abundance of fossil plant fragments (*Lepidodendron, Stigmaria* and *Calamites*) can be seen, both *in situ* in the sandstones and in the many loose blocks. Note the mechanical weathering of the sandstones by the numerous tree roots penetrating along bedding and joint planes.

Now follow the track up a small tributary of Bradshaw Brook, for approximately 60m (Figure 10) where (SD 736118) an exposure of boulder clay is seen with the vast majority of the clasts being of locally derived sandstone in a very sandy matrix.

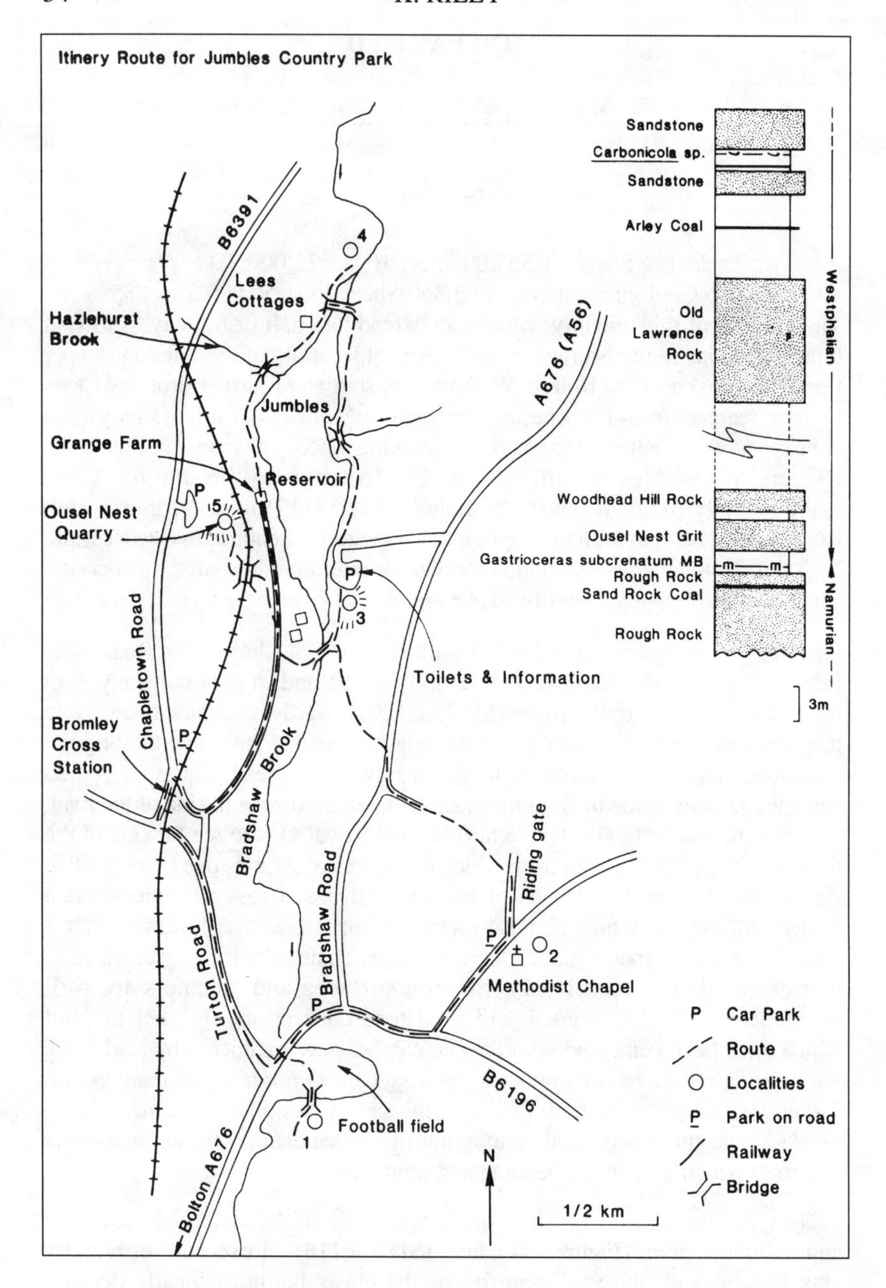

Figure 10. Sketch-map of the Jumbles area, Bolton.

Retrace steps to the A676 and continue eastwards. At the traffic lights proceed straight forward on the B6196 (signposted to Ainsworth). Note at the junction, high up on Bradshaw Chapel, a sandstone finger sign to Bolton. After half a kilometre turn left into Tottington Road, and thence walk northwest. At Tottington Road Methodist Church, at Harwood Lee, there is a small quarried exposure (SD 743124) in Westphalian A beds (**Locality 2**). Here, the Old Lawrence Rock is seen dipping 15 degrees to the south. This is an excellent place to measure true and apparent dip, and to determine the strike. Extensive bedding surfaces exhibit "rib and furrow" marks which have been produced by erosion of ripples. A short scramble up the path to the left (north) of the quarry reveals a much larger disused quarry (Hardy Mill Quarries) which at present is a landfill site and should not be entered. (It is hoped that eventually this tip will be landscaped to appear like Ousel Nest Quarry, **Locality 5**).

Cross over Tottington Road and almost opposite proceed down the *cul-de-sac*, Riding Gate, for approximately 100m. Take the signposted footpath on the left. At the main road turn right (north) and continue for approximately 250m. At a sign for the "West Pennine Moors" and "Bradshaw Bottoms" turn down the track on the left hand side of the road. The track eventually runs directly into a large disused quarry (SD 736138) at the southern end of Jumbles Reservoir (**Locality 3**).This overgrown quarry, in the Ousel Nest Grit (Westphalian A), exhibits planar cross-stratification on a much larger scale than that to be seen at the type locality Ousel Nest (**Locality 5**). The dip here is southerly. Note a very conspicuous erosion surface. At the northern end of the outcrop a fossil tree branch (preserved as a cast) can be seen about 2 metres above ground level. Look back down the Bradshaw valley and note the terraces.

Ascend the steps cut into the hillside alongside the reservoir embankment to the car park, and information centre. Jumbles Reservoir is a compensation reservoir for Bradshaw Brook ensuring a flow of 4 million gallons of water a day, the dam having been completed in 1971. Take the track northwards from the parking area past the information centre (restricted opening hours). Shortly a substantial bridge (SD 737143) over a tributary stream has to be crossed. If the water is low look at the mud flats for potential future trace fossils. From this point, the track follows the old, once cobbled road. Look out for glacial erratics of granites and tuffs from South Scotland and the Lake District.

At the northern end of the reservoir (SD 737148) another substantial bridge should be crossed. To the right (north) is a fine near-vertical section of Namurian rocks (**Locality 4**), access to which is gained by walking *around* the wooden fence near to the water edge. If the water level is very low the base of the section reveals the Sand Rock Coal, about 1 metre thick, which is cut by some excellent roof rolls, that is erosion channels, which do not extend to the base of the coal bed. The coal is overlain by approximately 10 metres of a coarse grained feldspathic (arkosic) sandstone, the upper leaf of the Rough Rock, the highest sandstone in the Namurian.

The section above the Rough Rock can be examined, with care, by traversing across a scree slope (SD 735150). The horizon of the Gastrioceras subcrenatum Marine Band (the base of the Westphalian) is not exposed here but typical Westphalian sediments are exhibited, namely sandstones, paper shales, mudstones, clay ironstone (siderite) nodules and a thin coal (about 5-10cm thick) with an underlying yellow seathearth. Fish scales have been found in the shales. Towards the left hand (southwest) end of the section (SD 735150), 2 metres of vertical fossil tree is exposed, the base concealed by debris. The bulk of the tree is preserved as a cast but the original bark and underlying woody tissues are preserved as coal. The tree was apparently overwhelmed by flooding and rapidly buried in its growth position.

Return to the path and continue around the western edge of the reservoir past Lees Cottages (SD 735148) with their Welsh slate roofs. Note the gable end where smoke rising up the chimneys has penetrated through the porous sandstone to blacken the outside of the stonework. Shortly, turn left over the bridge crossing Hazlehurst Brook to continue alongside the reservoir. Pass through Grange Farm (SD 733141) and its riding stables and continue along the tree-lined Grange road until a public footpath sign on the right indicates the way to Ousel Nest Quarry. Take the path, over a stile, across a field and under the single track railway. Continue along the metalled path until the access point through a wooden fence allows access to the quarry (SD 731141).

The quarry is some 100 metres wide and 300m long and now disused; the quarrying operations ceased when the working face reached the cottages on Prospect Hill on the B6391. With much forethought and vision the disused quarry area has been landscaped and provides a valuable recreational area for the adjacent houses.

This quarry is the type locality for the Ousel Nest Grit, the lowest sand body hereabouts, in Wesphalian A. Walk across the grass towards the far left hand side of the quarry noting an exposure of shale above the sandstone. This shale contains occasional layers of clay ironstone (siderite) concretions. Superb erosion channels are exposed in the underlying sandstones varying in depth from a few centimetres to over 3 metres. Note at the extreme left hand side of the exposure a coarsening-upwards sequence, only some 30 centimetres thick, which exhibits cross-stratification. On continuing further into the quarry some splendid near-horizontal slickensides become visible along a fault plane which here forms the southern quarry wall. At the far end of this wall there is a fault spring which continuously yields water, even in dry weather. The lush vegetation indicates the damp conditions. Another fault plane forms the north wall of the quarry and here, again, near-horizontal slickensides are seen. Inspection of the north wall of the quarry reveals that the sandstones are massive with no channels, being quite unlike the sandstones of the south wall, so there must have been some vertical movement on the faults to bring these two different facies into juxtaposition. Note also that the (poorly exposed) shales of the northern face lie at a different level from that of the corresponding shales in the southern face.

Retrace steps under the railway back to Grange Road (unmetalled) and continue in a southerly direction. Shortly a stile is reached (SD 733137) on the left hand (east) side with a sign for Jumbles Reservoir. If a vehicle has been left at Jumbles take the path which leads via **Locality 3** to the car park.

The return to Bromley Cross Station is made by continuing to the end of Grange Road. Turn right and in 20 metres the white gate, hidden until the last moment, gives access to the station platform.

ITINERARIES VIII to XI

Triassic rocks of the Cheshire Basin

D. B. Thompson

The object of the intineraries VIII to XI is to study and compare the stratigraphy, sedimentology and mineralisation of about 600m of Triassic strata exposed at Alderley Edge and in the Styal and Frodsham areas. The basic stratigraphy and sedimentology of the Cheshire Basin is illustrated in Table 4 which also explains the use of the abbreviations in the text which follows.

A bright foxy-red cross-bedded mottled sandstone facies exists alone in the Wilmslow Sandstone Formation (WSF). This facies is interbedded with cycles of darker-red pebbly sandstone facies in the Helsby Sandstone Formation (HSF). Throughout the area the palaeocurrents of the first facies are directed towards an arc lying between northwest and southwest, while in those of the latter facies the direction is between west through north to northeast (Thompson, 1966b, 1970b, 1985). It can be demonstrated that the mottled sandstone facies at some localities is aqueous, whereas at others it is totally aeolian, as at Frodsham (Thompson, 1969) where it was deposited by an easterly wind as the British Isles drifted northwards between 15° to 20° north of the palaeoequator (Robinson, 1971; Lovell, 1977). The dark red, often pebbly, cross-bedded sandstone was deposited by the migration of

Table 4
Stratigraphy and sedimentology of the Cheshire Basin:
(after Thompson, 1966b, 1970a, Warrington & Thompson, 1971, and Warrington, *et al.* 1980)

System	Stage	Group	Former nomenclature 1860 – 1980		Formations and members with thicknesses & abbreviations used in the text: Cheshire Basin generally	Formations and members with thicknesses & abbreviations used in the text: Alderley – Styal area	Sedimentology and palaeoenvironment
JURASSIC					LOWER & MIDDLE LIASSIC-Jur. c.600 m	Eroded	Shallow marine
TRIASSIC	Rhaetian	Penarth	RHAETIC BEDS			Eroded	Shallow marine, evaporitic in part
	NORIAN	MERCIA MUDST. GROUP MMG	UPPER KEUPER MARL	KEUPER	UNNAMED MUDSTONE FM c.300 m	Eroded	Hypersaline, lagoonal, Sabka, continental
			UPPER KEUPER Saliferous Beds	KEUPER	WILKESLEY HALITE FM c.400 m	Eroded	Salinas with marine feed
	CARNIAN		MIDDLE KEUPER MARL	KEUPER	UNNAMED MUDSTONE FM c.400 m	Eroded	Hypersaline, lagoonal, continental
	LADINIAN		LOWER KEUPER Saliferous Beds	KEUPER	NORTHWICH HALITE FM c.300 m	? Solution breccia	Salinas with marine feed
	ANISIAN		LOWER KEUPER MARL	KEUPER	UNNAMED MUDSTONE FM c.300 m	UNNAMED MUDSTONE FM	Hypersaline, lagoonal, continental
			WATERSTONES	KEUPER	TARPORLEY SILTSTONE FM, **TSF** c.120 m	TARPORLEY SILTSTONE FM, **TSF** c.120 m	Fluvial, intertidal, marine, hypersaline, lagoonal
	SCYTHIAN	THE SHERWOOD	LOWER KEUPER SANDSTONE	KEUPER	HELSBY SANDSTONE FM, **HSF** 100 – 150 m; Frodsham Soft Sst. Mbr **FSSM** c. 30 m	HELSBY SANDSTONE FM **HSF** c. 132 m; Nether Alderley Sst. Mbr **NASM** c. 38 m with Brynlow Conglom. at base c. 3 m	Fluvial, moderate sinuosity
					Delamere Pebbly Sandstone Member, **DPSM** c. 30 m	West Mine Sandstone Mbr, **WMSM** c.17 m	Aeolian dominates fluvial
						Wood Mine Conglom. Mbr, **WMCM** c 40 m	Fluvial, low sinuosity
					Thurstaston Soft Sst. Mbr, **TSSM** c. 30 m	Beacon Lodge Sst. Mbr. 12 m	Aeolian dominates fluvial
					with Thurstaston Hard Sst at base c. 3 m	Engine Vein Conglom. Mbr, **EVCM** 30 m	Fluvial; low-sinuosity, ephemeral
		SANDSTONE	BUNTER UPPER MOTTLED SANDSTONE	BUNTER	WILMSLOW SST. FM **WSF** c.300 m	WILMSLOW SST. FM **WSF** c.300 m	Aeolian dominates fluvial at top; Aeolian-fluvial; Fluvial dominates aeolian at base
		GROUP	BUNTER PEBBLE BEDS	BUNTER	CHESTER PEBBLE BED FM, **CPBF** c.200 m	CHESTER PEBBLE BED FM **CPBF** c.200 m	Fluvial, low-sinuosity, braided, very high discharges
? PERMIAN Upper	ZECHSTEIN 1 & ?2		MANCHESTER MARL	BUNTER	MANCHESTER MARL FM in the north 0-100 m; KINNERTON AND COLLYHURST SANDSTONE FM IN THE NORTH = BRIDGNORTH SST. IN THE SOUTH c.350 m	STOCKPORT & MANCHESTER MARLS 40-100 m	Marine with dwarfed restricted fauna, salinas with marine feed, some intertidal; Aeolian inland sand
PERMIAN Lower			BUNTER LOWER MOTTLED SANDSTONE FM	BUNTER		COLLYHURST SANDSTONE FM 150-275 m	Sea with dunes, draa and dry interdunes

large ripples on point and channel bars along low-sinuosity somewhat ephemeral river courses originating in the distant south. The conglomerates represent lag or race deposits in strong flood channels and the mudstone (formerly misnamed 'marl') bands indicate deposition in low-stage cut-off channels or swales within or across the whole of the river plain (Thompson, 1970b). The strata of the Tarporley Siltstone Formation (TSF) and Mercia Mudstone Group (MMG) generally are partly fluvial, but intertidal, lagoonal or truly marine influences were also present (Fitch, *et al.*, 1966; Ireland, *et al.*, 1978; Arthurton, 1980). The rocks outcrop on the northern flank of the Cheshire Basin whose gentle folding and subsequent faulting can be dated only as post-Liassic, pre-Pleistocene, probably Tertiary. In general the evolution of such basins has been dealt with by Gale, *et al.*, (1984), Ziegler (1981, 1982, 1988) and by Whittaker (1985).

ITINERARY VIII

Alderley Edge 1

Ordinance Survey 1:50,000 Sheet 118; 1:25,000 SJ 87/97
British Geological Survey 1:50,000 Sheet 98

This excursion is designed to illustrate the stratigraphy and sedimentology of the area (Table 4). The maps are also relevant to itinerary IX and the discussion below, on mineralisation, to itineraries IX and XI.

Alderley Edge is easily reached by bus or train from Manchester. The Edge, an escarpment lying to the east of Alderley and *c.* 25km south of Manchester, is formed partly by resistant HSF conglomerates and pebbly sandstones lying upon soft WSF and partly by the west-northwest — east-southeast and northwest — southeast normal faulting. The beds lie on the southern limb of the Wilmslow Anticline which plunges west-southwest. In detail the scarp is repeated eight times by faults throwing down to the northeast (Figure 14). The Edge lies within a horst which extends for *c.* 3km east-west, being terminated by powerful north—south faults which each throw *c.* 230m, the Kirkleyditch Fault to the east and the Alderley Fault to the west.

The Origins of the Minerals. The mineralisation, which is of hydrothermal type, is said to be *syngenetic* by some (i.e. introduced contemporaneously with the deposition and early lithification of the rock) (Bakewell, 1811, 1813; Hull, 1864; Roeder, 1901; Russell, 1919; Dewey & Eastwood, 1925; Ford, 1969) or *epigenetic* (emplaced subsequent to deposition and early lithification) (Greenwood, 1918, 1919, 1921; Taylor, *et al.*, 1963; Davidson,

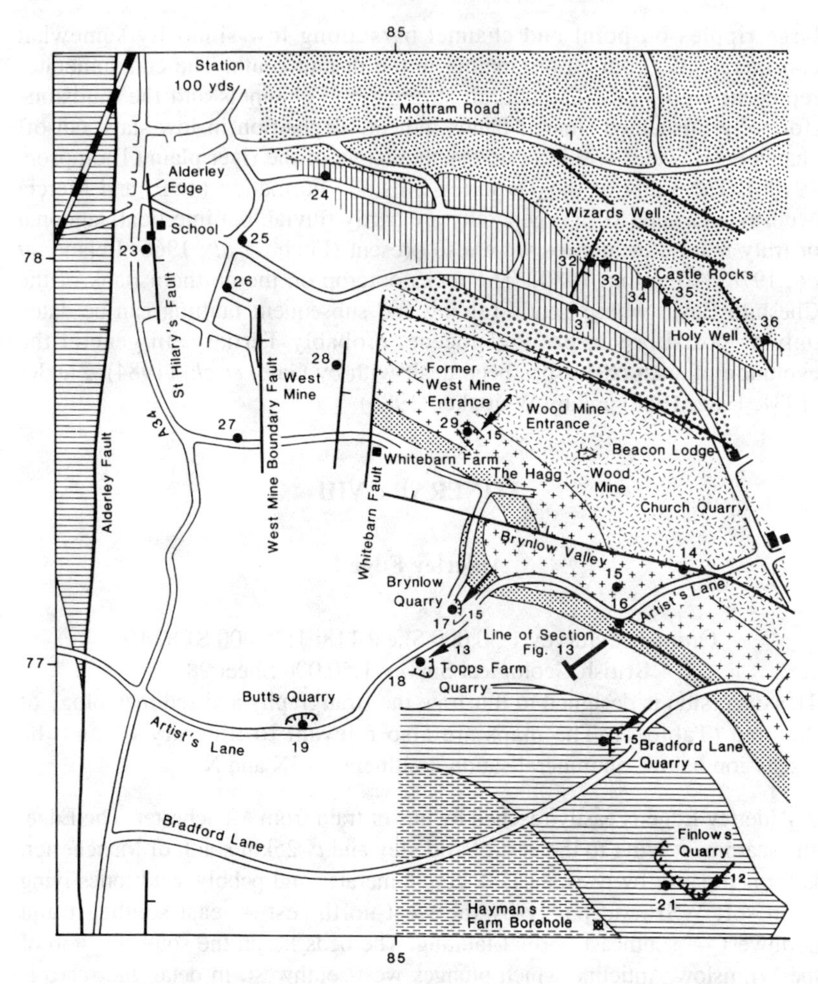

Figure 11. Geological map of the area around Alderley Edge, Cheshire, after the work of the British Geological Survey, with additions, including the inset map, from the work of D. B. Thompson. Areas where the geology is not well known are left blank.

1965, 1966; Warrington, 1965, 1980; Thompson, 1966c; Carlon, 1965, 1979; Carlon & Thompson, 1981; Ixer, 1978). Some authors favour a combination of syngenesis and epigenesis (Mohr, 1964; Ixer & Vaughan, 1982; Holmes, *et al.,* 1983; *cf.* King, 1966 and King & Ford, 1968).

Ixer (1978), Ixer & Vaughan (1982) and Holmes, *et al.*, (1983) give reasons for some mineralising events relating to early lithification

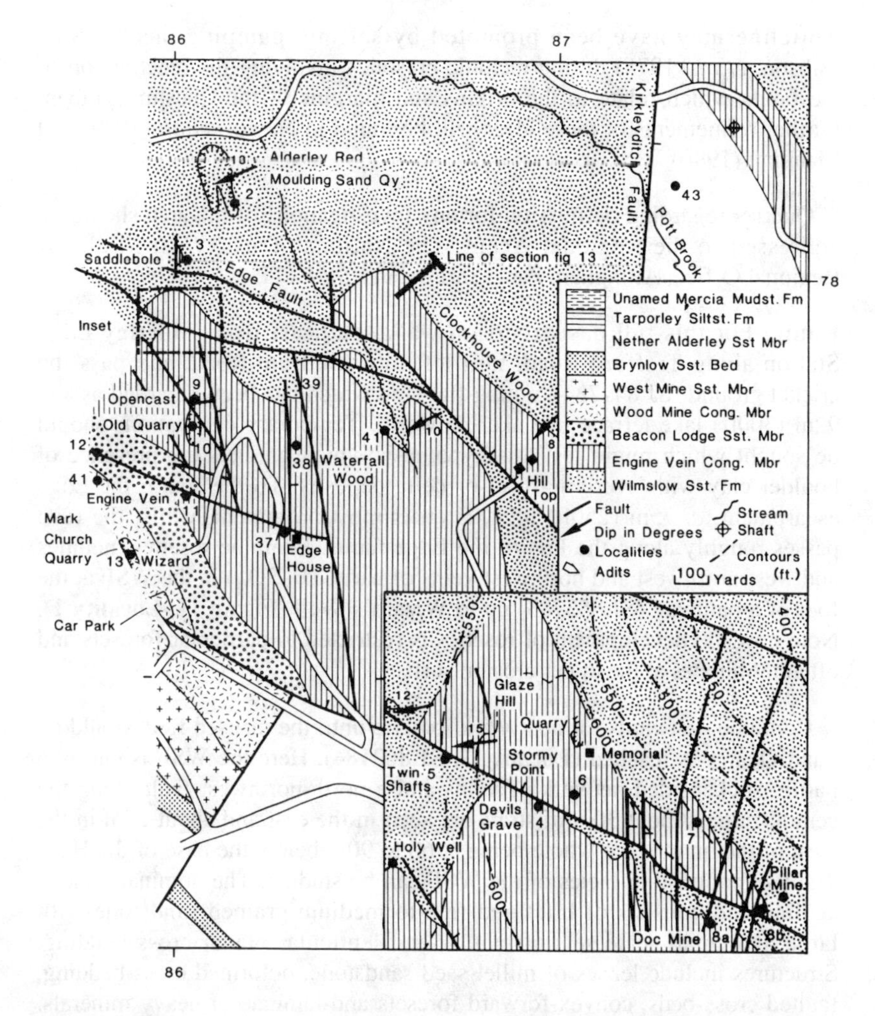

(=diagenesis) whilst they and others (Warrington, 1980; Carlon & Thompson, 1981) contemplate later (? late Jurassic to early Tertiary) mineralising events consequent upon the genesis of hydrocarbons and barium chloride brines bearing heavy metals in the Lower Palaeozoic and Carboniferous rocks beneath the Cheshire Basin, and the leaching of heavy metals by saline groundwaters from host mudstones (of the Mercia Mudstone Group) and sandstones (of the Sherwood Sandstone Group). Migration and crystallisation from these hydrocarbon-bearing and hydrothermal solutions along fault zones (largely west-northwest — east-southeast rather than north-south at Alderley) and in structural oil/gas traps like the faulted Wilmslow

Anticline may have been promoted by seismic-pumping mechanisms (Sibson, *et al.,* 1975) during tectonic episodes involving the reactivation of the faults which relate to the origins and margins of the Cheshire graben. Further refinements of these ideas will be found in Naylor, *et al.* (1989) and Manning (1990).

Queries regarding permission for any investigations of the area should be addressed to the Regional Agent, The National Trust, West Midlands Regional Office, Attingham Park, Shrewsbury SY4 4TP.

Route. For this full day excursion walk southeast from Alderley Edge Station along Trafford Road, turn left into Mottram Road, and pass the cricket ground (SJ 847784), noting flat land which has been regarded as a *c.* 92m (300ft) lake terrace of Lake Lapworth. Temporary excavations should be sought which might test this hypothesis which predicts the presence of boulder clay with overlying lake or delta deposits. To the south, the Edge escarpment, *c.* 75m (250ft) high, is at its most prominent, whilst the road passes roughly along the line of the Edge faults. Examine rosettes, nodules and west-northwest and northwest veins of barite ($BaSO_4$) in the WSF at the foot of a pathway (SJ 853783) up to Wizard's Well (Figure 11, **Locality 1**). Note how the development of rosettes is restricted to particular foresets and often terminates at the upper erosion surface.

Continue eastwards for nearly a kilometre until the disused Red Moulding Sand Quarry is reached (**Locality 2,** SJ 862184). Here the WSF is cut by a baritic slickensided network of veins and a north-northwest fault along the central ridge. About 30m of strata are seen in the east and about 25m in the west of the quarry, the whole being *c.* 60 to 90m below the base of the HSF. The two contrasting facies of the WSF can be studied. The dominant one is aeolian and consists of brick-red fine-to medium-grained sandstone with large and small-scale sets of tabular and lenticular planar cross-bedding. Structures include lenses of millet-seed sandstone, deformed cross-bedding, faulted cross-beds, convex-forward foresets and laminae of heavy minerals. The second facies in part aqueous, in part aeolian, is best seen at the base of the east side of the ridge. It consists of paler brick-red, fine-grained cross-bedded, flat-bedded sandstone interbedded with rare dark red mudstone laminae. Small-scale cross-beds contain millet-seeds and linear patches of granules, many of which are miniature ventifacts. Others have mudstone laminae which sometimes drape both the foresets and the ripple marks. Ripple bedding, ? wavy bedding-in-phase, convolute lamination and structureless bedding have been seen in the flat beds, deformation in the cross-beds, and flat lamination, mica and gritty inclusions in the mudstones. Cross-bedding is directed to *c.* 295°. A feature of the quarry is the close relation between the white mottling, the presence of barite, and faults or joints, for which there is a distinct north-south and west-northwest — east-southeast pattern traceable. Selective mottling of the foresets is seen high in the west side of the quarry close to the ridge.

Return to the Mottram Road, walk west 50 metres, and take the path up the hill to the west of the quarry on to Saddlebole (**Locality 3,** (SJ 860781). Examine an outlier which contains the junction of the Wilmslow Sandstone Formation (WSF) and the Engine Vein Conglomerate Member (EVCM). Walk southwards to Glaze Hill, where outcrops of veined and baritic EVCM are seen along the old saddle road running south-southeast to Stormy Point (SJ 860778). Here, there is a magnificent view to the east over a landslip which was possibly initiated on this northeast side during the freeze-thaw conditions of post-Pleistocene. Four episodes of fluvial (EVCM) sedimentation can easily be recognised here. The first, represented by the basal marl, is at it thickest at Devil's Grave (**Locality 4**, SJ 860778). The second, comprises a pebbly sandstone, whose base, with irregular corrasion furrows, can be well observed at and within Devil's Grave and Twin Shafts (**Locality 5,** SJ 859779). This unit, with rolled ventifacts, galls, armoured mudballs, large lenticular planar cross-beds, sometimes deformed (Figure 12, inset map, point x), is capped by a richly micaceous mudstone band (Fitch, *et al.,* 1966, but see Mitchell & Taka, 1984), and can be studied at Twin Shafts, Devil's Grave, on Stormy Point (**Locality 6**), to the southeast of the landslip (**Locality 7**), and within and above Doc Mine (**Locality 8** SJ 861778)). The third and fourth episodes, similar to the second, can be seen on Stormy Point and at **Locality 7**, where the intervening 'marl' band is missing. On the north side of Pillar Mine entrance (**Locality 8b**) the lowest cycle of EVCM is virtually a gravel.

This is a convenient spot to study the pebbles themselves. Up to 15 per cent show influence of wind abrasion (fluting, polishing, facetting) (Thompson & Worsley, 1967); 59 per cent are quartzites, some carrying Lower Palaeozoic fossils; 34 per cent are pebbles of vein quartz; 7 per cent are rarer types including black quartzites, cherts containing Carboniferous corals and crinoids, porphyries, felsites, rare granite, reworked sandstone, siltstone, grit, cataclastic breccia, tourmaliniferous rocks of many types and schistose quartzite. Most pebbles are disc- or spheroid-shaped, a few are rod-shaped and a few are bladed. Many are re-worked Bunter pebbles from the Midlands. They derive ultimately from the Palaeozoic rocks of the Midlands and the superstructure of Armorica in southern England, the Channel and northern France (Greenwood, 1919; Thompson, 1966b, 1970b). **Locality 8b** has a excellent *c.* 17m section of the WSF in which variations of porosity and permeability in the aeolian dune and interdune deposits greatly influence the incidence of Cu and Co-Ni mineralisation.

Climb southwards, cross the main bridleway, pass Opencast Mine (SJ 860777) and enter Old Alderley Quarry (**Locality 10** SJ 867776), walking all the way over the lowest 15m of EVCM, which is repeatedly upthrown on the south by normal faults. This quarry displays the third and fourth episodes of EVCM sedimentation. Here, there are few pebbles and the main interest centres on the 'marl' band and the sandstone surfaces above and below it. The red micaceous shale, which has yielded *Euestheria,* is split by 10cm of sandstone at the north end, but fails completely to the southwest, where it is cut out by a shallow erosion channel. To the south lies Engine Vein (**Locality 11** SJ 860774), which is the type section of the basal conglomerates which are yet again upthrown on the south side by two parallel faults *c.* 60m apart. The strata formerly exposed in this section (Carlon, 1979, 92-101) are illustrated in detail in Figure 12. For reasons of public safety, most of the lower openworks have had to be sealed off by a concrete raft and access for serious parties is controlled for the National Trust by the Derbyshire Caving Club (contact Stephen Mills at Rose Bank, Peover Lane, Chelford SK11 9AW (0625) 861502, or Nigel Dibbens, 62 Middlewich Road, Holmes Chapel (0477) 347772). The lowest *c.* 13.5 m of EVCM were succeeded by a single bed of mottled sandstone facies, and then, at the western end by *c.* 13m of poorly exposed repetitions of white sandstone and green-red clay. This type of river-plain top-stratum deposit was found to occupy the whole of the lowest 31.5m of the Haymans Farm borehole (1963) (SJ 856764) and hence represents the lateral equivalent of the 30m of fluvial channel-fill strata of the EVCM in the area of Victorian Alderley, one mile to the west. Warrington (1963, 1967) reported *Euestheria* and plant spores of late Scythian age from these clay-beds. Continue west-northwest for 300m towards Beacon Lodge (SJ 857775), where *c.* 12m of typical mottled sandstone between the EVCM and Wood Mine Conglomerate Member (WMCM) is exposed in a northeast-trending path which is cut by the baritic west-northwest Engine Vein fault (**Locality 12,** SJ 858777). Walk south-southeast along Macclesfield Road to the Wizard Restaurant (SJ 895773), and seek permission to enter Church Quarry (**Locality 13,** SJ 858773) immediately to the north-northwest. The lowest two cycles of the nine of the WMCM are separated by a mudstone band which is partially cut out by an irregular erosion surface which approaches channel dimensions to the north-northwest. Remnants of the band are found as huge clay galls and mudballs, armoured in part with rolled ventifacts, on the west wall. A blind adit is found where barite mineralisation is strongest. The road to the east of the Wizard displays some of the less common vein and joint directions of the area. The well shaft to the north of the Wizard has been recently shown to be an entry shaft to the long-lost cobalt mine described by Bakewell (1811, 1813; Johnson, 1984). This mine, the Wizard (Restaurant) Well Cobalt Mine (SJ 859773) extends for over 0.5km north-

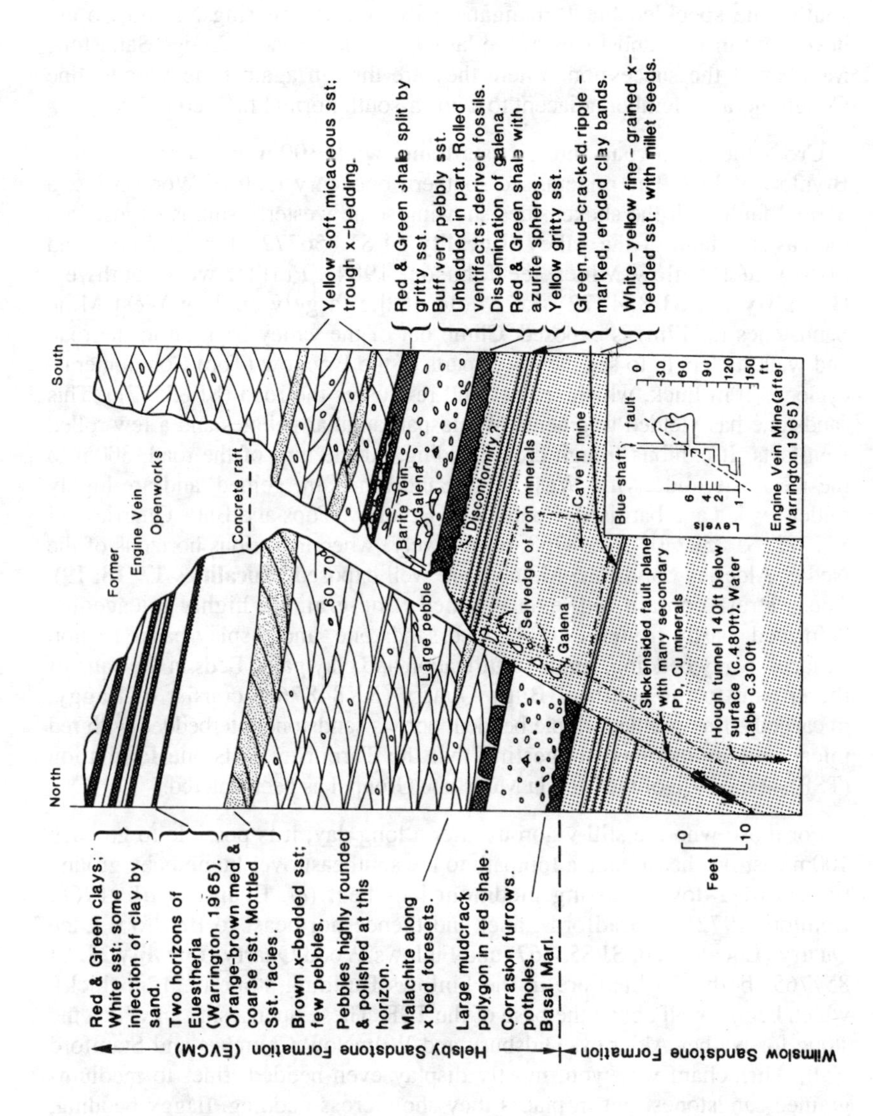

Figure 12. Diagrammatic section across Engine Vein, Locality 11 of Figure 11. The base of the Helsby Sandstone Formation is regarded as the Hardegsen unconformity by some (cf. Colter & Barr, 1975), but it may merely represent a change of facies associated with a deep-cut fluvial channel (Taylor, et al., 1963, Thompson, 1970a). Note that mineralisation affects both the WSF and the HSF (EVCM), a fact not always appreciated in old accounts of syngenetic mineralisation.

south. The speckled black manganese hydroxides bearing Ni and Co are developed in red sandstones of the largely aeolian Beacon Lodge Sandstone Member of the succession, where they are thrown against the Wood Mine Conglomerate Member adjacent to a north-south normal fault complex.

Cross the main road into Artists Lane, walk 300m and turn right into Brynlow Valley. The mineralised southern boundary fault of Wood Mine, a normal fault with the slickensides showing some westerly slip, is exposed on the eastern flank of the valley (**Locality 14** SJ 856772), for the nature and history of Brynlow Mines see Johnson, 1984). Further west-southwest (**Locality 15,** SJ 854772) the whole of the largely aeolian West Mine Sandstones (*c.* 17m) is exposed. Climb out of the valley back on to the road and walk its length to see the lower parts of the Brynlow (Top) Conglomerate cycle, *c.* 10m thick, which crosses and re-crosses the road (SJ 855771). This sandstone has yielded fragments of feldspar, angular pebbles and a few rolled ventifacts. It exhibits trough cross-bedding. At the turn of the road, 300m to the west, the underlying West Mine Sandstones are veined, and are highly millet-seeded and baritised. Continue to Brynlow, Tops and Butts Quarries (SJ 851772, SJ 850770, SJ 848768, respectively) wherein various horizons of the Nether Alderley Sandstone Member are well exposed (**Localities 17, 18, 19**). These strata contain red, even-grained, fine-grained, highly micaceous, deformed, partly trough cross-bedded sandstone, and display basal erosion surfaces, wavy bedding, ripple stratification and clay galls. Beds in the bank of the stream to the south of Butts Quarry (SJ 848768) consist of flaggy, micaceous, fine-grained, ripple bedded, porous sandstone interbedded with red micaceous mudstones, suggesting that the Tarporley Siltstone Formation (TSF), at the base of the Mercia Mudstone Group, has been entered.

For those who are still vigorous after a long day, it is possible to go back 100m east-northeast, take a footpath to the southeast over hummocky ground typical of a down-wasting piedmont ice-sheet (*cf.* Evans, *et al.,* 1968; Boulton, 1972) to Bradford Lane, and thence northeast to Bradford Lane Quarry (**Locality 20,** SJ 855767) and Finlows Wood Quarry (**Locality 21,** SJ 857765) both of which are in the Finlows Building stone (*c.* 12m thick), which begins well above the base of the TSF. These quarries, from which the stone for Nether Alderley, Didsbury and Wilmslow Churches and Stamford Hall, Altrincham was won, mostly display even-bedded, fine- to medium-grained sandstones, but in places they show cross-bedding, flaggy bedding, micaceous partings, clay galls, zoned mudballs and wedges of red shale. A few trace fossils (vertical and horizontal burrows) have been detected in these beds at outcrop and others were seen in equivalent beds in the nearby Hayman's Farm borehole (SJ 856764) in 1963 (see Appendix in Thompson, 1966b; *cf.* Pollard, 1981). Interbedded flaggy sandstones and shales, the highest beds, occur in the south face of the quarry.

ITINERARY IX

Alderley Edge 2

Before attempting this itinerary, which is designed to illustrate mineralisation and structure, it is worthwhile examing the display of ores and sediments in the special exhibit in the Manchester Museum and carrying in hand Carlon's book, "The Alderley Edge Mines" (Carlon, 1979).

Walk southward along the A34 to the entrance of St. Hilary's School, Alderley Edge (Figure 11). Note the mottled baritic Wilmslow Sandstone Formation (WSF) on the east side of the A34 (**Locality 23,** SJ 843781). This is related to St. Hilary's Fault aligned north-south at the back of the school. Face westward and note that the north-facing scarp terminates abruptly 100m to the west beyond the houses. This steep west-facing slope, 2.5km long north to south, is the line of the Alderley Fault, a fault-line scarp formed by a normal fault throwing the Mercia Mudstone Group (MMG) of the low ground to the west against the older Helsby Sandstone Formation (HSF). Turn northeast and walk up Chapel Road to Trafford Road, then turn right as far as Woodbrook Road. Examine the Engine Vein Conglomerate Member (EVCM) with baritic veins and rosettes 100m to 200m up the road (**Locality 24,** SJ 847782). Return to Trafford Road and walk south to the Macclesfield Road (**Locality 25,** SJ 845780), where in EVCM there is an interesting lag and erosion surface. Walk directly south for 150m, turn left and examine Beacon Lodge Sandstones in the pathway (**Locality 26,** SJ 845779). Continue eastwards for 100m and then turn southwards for 0.4km, walking approximately along the line of the West Mine Boundary Fault. Reach Whitebarn Road, turn right and note outcrops of Brynlow (=Top) Conglomerate by the telegraph pole (**Locality 27,** SJ 846775) before turning eastwards and walking over the main working of West Mine, 30m below ground, to Whitebarn Farm. Digress due north for 170m to a knoll (**Locality 28,** SJ 848777) where a low ridge of baritic millet-seeded West Mine Sandstone ends abruptly against one of the north-south faults through West Mine. Return to Whitebarn Farm and continue to walk east-southeast for 320m until a flat sandy heath is reached.

Unheralded immediately to the south of the path lies the southern boundary fault of both West and Wood Mines. 100m to the north, once lay the most imposing West Mine entrance (**Locality 29,** SJ 851776) now covered by landfill materials (Carlon, 1979, pp. 55-82, especially the photographs and diagrams, pp. 58-63, 73-77). The ownership of this mine is now in the hands of Mr. Paul Sorensen of Whitebarn, Whitebarn Road, Alderley Edge SK9 7AY. For *bona fide* parties, permission to visit the mine may be sought from the owner and arrangements made with Mr. Stephen Mills (address on p. 64) of the Derbyshire Caving Club for safe passage through the mine. Minerals which have been found here are listed in Table 5. Roscoe (1868-9, 1976) studied highly vanadiferous sandstone from hereabouts.

From West Mine walk eastwards towards the entrance of Wood Mine (**Locality 30,** SJ 854775). Warrington (1965) has shown that mineralisation affects at least eight fluvial cycles of the Wood Mine Conglomerate Member (WMCM) lying between the west-northwest–east-southeast trending southern and northern boundary faults which are *c.* 400m apart. The east-west extent of the mineralisation appears to be *c.* 300m. Mineralisation is best developed near the faults. Refer to Table 5 for the minerals present. From here walk northeast, reach the main road and turn left for 0.4km. Walk *c.* 110m northeast to **Locality 31,** (SJ 855778) and the viewpoint at Castle Rocks (**Locality 32,** SJ 856779). Climb down to the path below and observe *c.* 8m of fluvial EVCM lying above a pronounced erosion surface (? a disconformity) heavily baritic and rich in nodules, patches and rosettes lying upon *c.* 4m of WSF of aeolian facies, wherein are preserved the lowermost parts of what were once very large sand dunes. These are interbedded with wavy, flat-bedded sandstones. The base of the EVCM is marked by an impersistent mudstone which can be traced westwards.

A walk towards Wizards Well, *c.* 100m to the west, (SJ 855780), enables variations of the EVCM to be traced. The second mudstone band in the succession 25m east of the Well (**Locality 33,** SJ 855780) has fascinating internal lithological variations. The sandstone undersurface above this band bears strong mudcracks and possible organic marks. It is best to take plasticine casts of interesting features. The scoured surface above the third mudstone band displays irregular corrasion furrows. At Wizards Well (**Locality 34**) a terraced erosion channel is seen cutting the first mudstone band and alongside is an excellent example of a north-south slickensided normal fault with a discernible throw of *c.* 15m to the east. Note that the first impermeable mudstone band, holding up a perched water table at 165m (540 ft) O.D., some 73m above the general water table of the area, gives rise to a spring. The cause of the scarp is obvious.

Return to Castle Rocks and walk 90m along the lower path until a sculpted face is located (**Locality 35,** SJ 856778). Alongside this are two highly baritic north-northwest normal faults. Two hundred metres farther southeast, in the vicinity of the wall of the reservoir, (SJ 857777) is the farthest northwest extension in the Alderley area of malachite mineralisation. This is associated with small normal and rare reverse faults which were observed in the reservoir excavation in 1911. From here descend 120m northeast down the scarp, cross the valley which marks the line of the Holy Well fault and examine the crags, perched water table, two springs and landslipped blocks of EVCM at Holy Well (**Locality 36,** SJ 859778), inset map, Figure 12). Note the deformed, cross-bedded argillaceous sandstone in the quarried area on the east side of the upper crags at a horizon equivalent to the second mudstone band elsewhere. Cross a further small north-northwest fault, climb northwards and upwards 12m in 60m to Twin Shafts (**Locality 5,** SJ 859779, inset map), and see the strongly mineralised extension of the slickensided north-northwest Stormy Point normal fault throwing to the north-northeast. Good mineral specimens may be found in the mine spoil (see Table 5) and are derived largely from the basal four cycles of the EVCM. Climb above the mine, walk north-northeast along the west side of Glaze Hill (inset map), noting numerous strongly baritic north-northwest joints and small faults, and reach Saddlebole (**Locality 3,** SJ 860781) a former smelting hearth open to west winds and the site of an outlier of EVCM, which is not mapped on the 1:10560 Geological Survey Map. It houses the most northerly mine of the area, this time developed in the WSF. Return via the east side of Glaze Hill to the vicinity of the Pilkington Memorial on Stormy Point (**Locality 6,** SJ 860779), and relocate the veins and slickensided Stormy Point fault which is clearly mineralised. Pb and Cu sulphides are known along the main fault line hereabouts. Follow the sinuous course of the main fault and its splays for 100m to the east-southeast, crossing four north-south faults, until the entrances of Doc Mine (**Locality 8a**) and Pillar Mine (**Locality 8b,** SJ 861778) are reached. The mouths of both mines show secondary Cu mineralisation, the former in the basal EVCM, the latter in the top 15m of the WSF, both to the south of the fault. Immediately north of the Pillar Mine entrace, in the EVCM on the downthrown side of the fault, a bed of gravel shows up to 30 per cent barite. The spoil tips yield rich pickings of mineralised sandstone samples. From here climb the scarp and walk 110m south-southwest, crossing a roadway until the fault gulley of Opencast (**Locality 9,** SJ 860777) is reached. Here the basal EVCM bears cerussite. Continue to walk southward through Old Alderley Quarry (**Locality 10,** SJ 867776), across a small fault on the north side of a small quarry (SJ 860775) and reach the site of the former Engine Vein openworks and mine (Carlon, 1979, pp. 92-101). Permission to gain access to the mines by parties with serious investigations in mind can be sought through the Derbyshire Caving Club (contact Stephen Mills, address on p. 64).

Here (Figure 13, **Locality 11**), the mineralisation follows a west-northwest fault (throw 7m to the north) whose slickensided surface is well seen and affects both the WSF and the HSF (EVCM). There is a greater degree and variety of mineralisation here than elsewhere (Table 5). Sulphides of Pb, Cu and Zn (with As, Ni, Co and Ag) are concentrated near the fault and

Table 5 Mineral species found at Alderley Edge and Mottram St. Andrews Mines.

ELEMENTS	COPPER MINERALS Cu +																											
	S								CO_3		SO_2		As					SO_4						P_2	O_2	Pb VZr		CO_3 Zn
MINERALS / PLACES	CHALCOPYRITE	BORNITE	CHALCOCITE	COVELLITE	BLAUBLEIBENDER COVEL	DJURLEITE	IDEATITE	TENNANTITE	MALACHITE	AZURITE	CHRYSOCOLLA	PLANCHEITE	ENARGITE	POSNJAKITE	LIROCONITE	OLIVENITE	TYROLITE	ANTLERITE	BROCHANTITE	LANGITE	CALEDONITE	LINARITE	PISANITE	LIBETHENITE	CUPRITE	NATIVE COPPER	MOTTRAMITE	AURICHALCITE
WEST MINE	• RB	•							•	•	• RB						• RB											
NEW VENTURE LEVEL									•	•																		
WOOD MINE	•	? (see I & V p. 489)	?	?	?	?	?		•	•	•					•	• RB		• RB						?			• RB
ENGINE VEIN	•	•	•	•	•	•	•		•	•	•	• AK	•	•	?	•		• RB	• RB	• RB	? 1	•	•	•	• PR	• PR		
OPENCAST									•	•																		
DOC AND PILLAR MINE									•	•									• RB									
STORMY POINT	•	? (see I & V p. 489)	?	?	?	?	?		•	•															?			
TWIN SHAFTS																												
KIRKLEYDITCH									•	•																		•
UNSPECIFIED LOCALITIES	•							•														•						

Order of abancance of ore metals (Mohr, 1944): Cu (most common), Pb, Ba, Mn, Co, Ca, Fe, Zn, Ni, V.

Finds authenticated since 1966 by:

RB = R. S. W. Braithwaite
I & V = Rob Ixer & D. Vaughan
AK = Arthur Kingsbury
PR = Peter Robinson
GH = G. Harwood
RI = Rob Ixer
JRK = J. R. Knight
N = Naylor, *et al.*

★★ pararammelbergite, Ni-cobaltite Gerdorfite Fe arsenate

TABLE 5 *continued*

ELEMENTS	LEAD MINERALS Pb+										Zn+			Fe+									Mn Ni Co+				OTHER MINERALS including GANGUE						
	S	CO_3 – SO_4			O_2		P_2O_5		Wo	V	S	SiO_2	CO_3	S		S-Ni-Co-As			H_2O	SO_4	Ag		H_2O		As	S							
MINERALS / PLACES	GALENA	CERRUSITE	LEADHILLITE	ANGLESITE	MINIUM	MASSICOT	PYROMORPHITE	AS-PYROMORPHITE	WULFENITE	VANADINITE	SPHALERITE	HEMIMORPHITE	SMITHSONITE	MARCASITE	PYRITE	BRAVOITE	Ni-Co-Fe	PHARMACOSIDERITE	LIMONITE	SCORODITE	ARGENT-TETRAHEDRITE	NATIVE SILVER	WAD	ASBOLITE	ERYTHRITE	NICKEL ARSENIDES	BARITE	WITHERITE	GYPSUM	CALCITE	JAROSITE	NATIVE SULPHUR	HYDROCARBONS
WEST MINE	•	•							• RB	★ • GH									•				•	•			•						
NEW VENTURE LEVEL	•	•																	•				•	•			•						
WOOD MINE	•	•		? I&V			•	• RB	• RB			• RB	? I&V		•	•			•		? I&V		•	•	• RB		•						
ENGINE VEIN	•	•	• RB	•	•	•	•	• RB	• RB		•	• RB	• RI	•	•	•	•	• RB	•	•	• RI	• JRK	•	•	•	• RI	•	•	•	•	•	• RB	RB
OPENCAST	•	•																	•				•	•			•						
DOC AND PILLAR MINE	•						•												•								•						
STORMY POINT	•			? I&V							•		? I&V	•	•	•	•		•		•						•						
TWIN SHAFTS	•																		•								•						
KIRKLEYDITCH	•	•					•			•									•				•	•			•						?
UNSPECIFIED LOCALITIES	• N									?	• N																			• N			

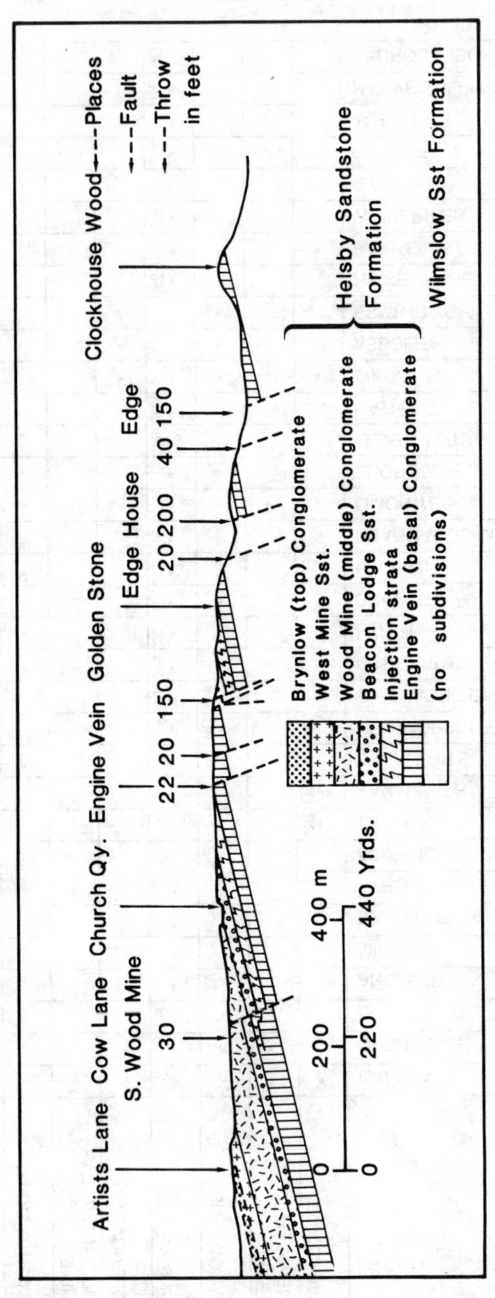

Figure 13. Section across Alderley Edge.

especially occupy a vertical 0.60m band in the adjacent WSF parallel to the fault and a horizontal area in EVCM on the south side of the fault. Reworked and ?secondary oxides, hydrous oxides, carbonates, sulphates and silicates of Pb and Cu are present along and adjacent to the fault. A unique feature is the development of azurite spheres in the red and green sandy shale at the base of the EVCM. On the north side of the fault, malachite is seen to occupy cross-strata preferentially and to be 'cut off' at the overlying erosion surface. The same is true of asbolite (earthy cobalt) in the WSF in the cave on the south side of the fault, now underneath the concrete safety raft.

Turn eastwards, reach the track to the east of Engine Vein, walk 70m to the south and take the path east-northeast across the field to the north of Edge House Farm (SJ 863774). Immediately north of the farm the surface of the track-way bears evidence of anastomosing baritic veins for a width of *c.* 4m (**Locality 37,** SJ 863774). Cross the stile and turn northwards past Edge House Quarry (**Locality 38,** SJ 863776), which shows *c.* 3m of baritic EVCM, in some places shattered and jointed due to the proximity of a small fault. Return to Edge House and walk along the track and pathway northwards into Dickens Wood, and examine radiating veins on the east side of the dry valley in the WSF (**Locality 39,** SJ 863777). Return to the path above Dickens Wood and walk north-east to the mouth of Waterfall Wood (SJ 864779), where EVCM is downfaulted to the level of a stream in whose bed it is possible to locate yet another north-south baritic fault. Climb south-southeast for 320m upvalley into Waterfall Wood, passing prominent crags of EVCM (SJ 865779) through which an artificial saddle road (ore routeway) was cut. Cross the Edge Fault and locate an excellent outcrop on the west side of the valley. At **Locality 41** (SJ 865776) the WSF reveals an unusually large *c.* 3.5m thick set of cross-bedding, with intraset cross-beds, deformed strata, millet-seed lenses and a high degree of sorting, lying upon relatively horizontal strata. These beds may represent small dunes migrating down the faces of very large dunes, known as draa (*cf.* Brookfield, 1977, 1985). Climb out of the Wood via the waterfall, noting the barite veins, and take the path across the Edge Fault to the south end of Clockhouse Wood, where yet another scarp is apparent (**Locality 42,** SJ 868777).

Walk from here direct to Kirkleyditch, crossing the fault of that name as the recreation ground is reached (**Locality 43,** SJ 872783). In this fault block the stratigraphy hereabouts, and to the south along Pottbrook, is comparable with that in the Alderley horst (Thompson, 1970a, figure 5). This is the site of the former treatment works of Mottram Mine (Carlon, 1979, p.115), and from here an adit extended east-northeast. Spoil heaps abound and mineral samples can still be found (see Table 5). Little is known of this mine (but see Greenwell, 1866 and Warrington, 1981), and it is not clear where faults or oreshoots lie in relation to the present ground. The old quarry in EVCM, now in the grounds of a private house (Copperfields), is weakly mineralised. It was here that the presence of asbolite (of use in glass-making) was discovered by a miner who had seen similar ores in Saxony in the 1800s. Ores of a tenor up to 22 per cent Cu were once mined. It is likely that the vanadium minerals roscoellite, mottramite and vanadinite were found here by Roscoe (1868-9, 1876) as a result of being transported from Pim Hill, north of Shrewsbury, for processing and smelting, though specimens from West Mine might equally well have been smelted too (see also Kingsbury, *in* Kingsbury & Hartley, 1956).

Return to Alderley westwards for 3km along Mottram Road.

ITINERARY X

Styal area, Cheshire

Ordnance Survey 1:50,000 Sheet 109; 1:25,000 SJ 88/89
British Geological Survey 1:50,000 Sheet 98

The strata outcrop in a gorge and plateau near the River Bollin, 13km south of Manchester. They dip northwest and lie on the northwest limb of the Wilmslow anticline, whose axis is aligned east-northeast — west-southwest. Powerful normal faulting and slight mineralisation can be observed.

Styal is a showpiece of the National Trust, being a creation of Hubert Greg who, needing waterpower, sited his textile mill at Quarrybank, adjacent to the gorge in 1784 (Rose, 1986). The mill now houses an industrial museum which is managed by a trust. The village grew as a self-contained community in the van of the industrial revolution, and though modernised within, has its exterior preserved as of old. Enquiries concerning visits should be made to the Trust Manager, Quarrybank Mill, Styal. **Hammering is forbidden on National Trust land.**

Route. Styal may be reached by road or rail from Manchester. Cars should be parked for the day in the place provided in the village or in the car park northeast of the Mill (SJ 836831, Figure 14). From the National Trust car park (SJ 836831) walk south past the reservoir (SJ 835829) over the till of late Würm age, noting erratics of Lake District and Southern Uplands type, some of them ventifacts. The view to the southeast reveals the northeast facing scarp of Alderley Edge on the southern limb of the anticline. Here, the rocks of comparable age have no surface expression as a scarp feature, possibly because conglomeratic horizons in the Helsby Sandstone Formation are weakly developed, but more likely because of erosional events in the early Pleistocene (Gresswell, *in* Smith, 1953, and especially the rather differing accounts of subsequent glacial events at the end of the Devensian by Taylor, *et al.*, 1963 and by Evans, *et al.*, 1968). Continue along the path to Twinnies Bridge (SJ 838823) where outwash sands within or below the till can be examined in abandoned pits (Figure 14, **Locality 1,** SJ 838823). The Alderley Fault, bounding the Styal graben on the east, has no surface expression, but passes north to south 200m east of the bridge. Turn westwards through a stile into a wood, noting a large granite erratic to the left of the path (SJ 837823) and outcrops of typical Wilmslow Sandstone Formation, cross-bedding directed to 275°, at a bluff on the south bank of the river (SJ 836823). Heavy minerals from the WSF at Wilmslow suggest affinity with types found at comparable horizons in the Midlands (Alty, 1926).

Continue westwards to **Locality 2** (SJ 835823), where basal pebbly sandstones of the HSF are exposed. In contrast to 10 cycles (*c.* 30m thick) at Alderley, a single cycle (*c.* 4m thick) is found (Thompson, 1970a, figures 4 and 5). Note the basal erosion surface, a fluvial channel floor and the thinning of cross-bed sets upward. Search amongst the larger clasts should reveal similar proportions of pebble types and rolled ventifacts as will be found at Alderley. Cross-bedding is directed towards 324°. A few metres to the west these beds are succeeded by *c.* 5m of flat-bedded mottled sandstone, and a thicker continuation of this facies, with more cross-bedding and wavy bedding, is found throughout the length of Badger Hole (**Locality 3,** SJ 834824). These beds are the equivalent of those near Beacon Lodge, Alderley, but are much thicker. Abundant millet-seed grains indicate aeolian influence and characteristic lamination types (*cf.* Hunter, 1977) suggest aeolian dune and interdune deposition. Cross-bedding is directed towards 275°. A small fault and veins bearing barite (barytes) and wad (earthy cobalt with manganese) are also to be seen here.

Walk north-northwest to Worms Hill building stone quarry (**Locality 4,** SJ 833825), which exposes *c.* 15m of the HSF (Delamere Pebbly Sandstone Member) from which the stone to build the Mill was taken. At the south end an uncemented argillaceous horizon is eroded away and structures of uncertain origin are seen on the base of the overlying bed. A micaceous marl band in the northwest of the quarry is split by wedges of pebbly sandstone. Rolled ventifacts and zoned mudballs have been found in the thick-bedded sandstone which has trough, lenticular planar and wedge cross-bedding of fluvial origins. It is more massive and varied than usual. Continue north-northwest, noting how the river has taken advantage of the Styal Fault, and

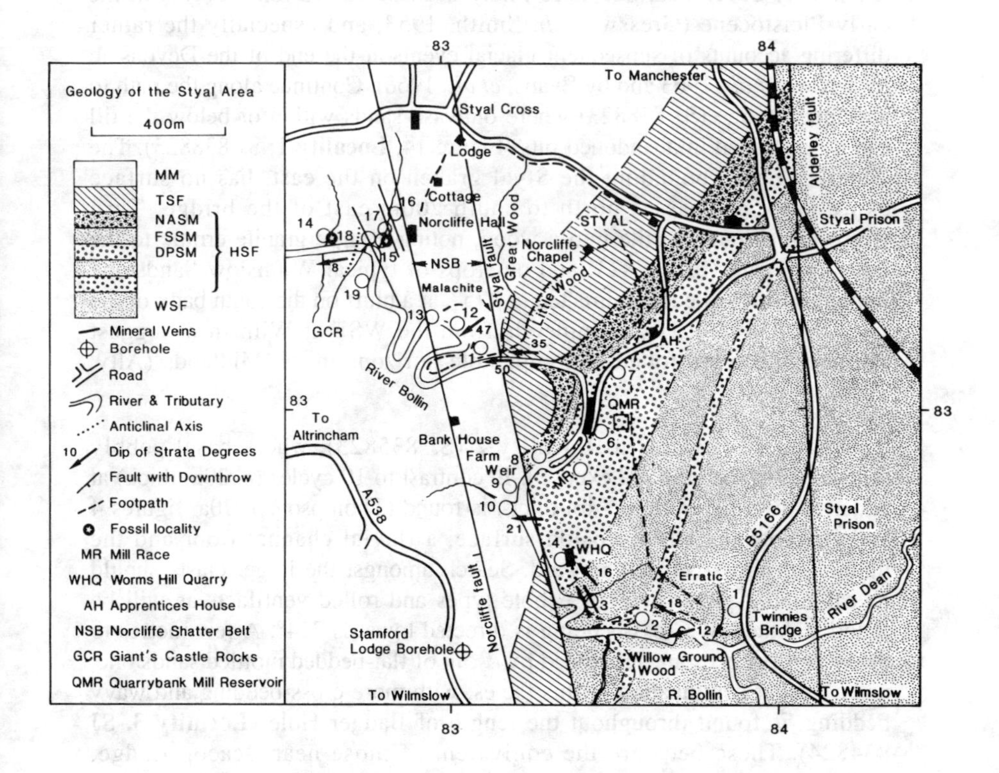

Figure 14. Geological map of the area around Styal, Cheshire, after the British Geological Survey, with additions from the work of D. B. Thompson.

MM = unnamed mudstone formation c. 306m (= 1000 ft) thick (formerly the Lower Keuper Marl) in the Mercia Mudstone Group.

TSF = Tarporley Siltstone Formation c. 116m (= 380 ft) thick (formerly the 'Keuper' Waterstones) at the base of the Mercia Mudstone Group.

HSF = Helsby Sandstone Formation c. 125m (= 410 ft) thick (formerly the Lower 'Keuper' Sandstone) at the top of the Sherwood Sandstone Group.

The fine dotted ornament in the outcrop of the HSF denotes the presence of unnamed soft sandstone units largely of aeolian origin. The circles denote the presence of pebbly sandstone units largely of fluvial origin. Named rock units are: NASM = Nether Alderley Sandstone Member; FSSM = Frodsham Soft Sandstone Member; DPSM = Delamere Pebbly Sandstone Member.

WSF = Wilmslow Sandstone Formation c. 367m (=1200 ft) thick (formerly the 'Bunter' Upper Mottled Sandstone) in the Sherwood Sandstone Group.

turn north-northeast to examine three exposures of the uppermost pebbly cycle of the DPSM (*c.* 12m) exposed at **Localities 5, 6** and **7,** before and past the Mill. At **Locality 5** (SJ 838828) the lowest pebbly beds are seen in the gully of the tributary stream, while higher mudstones interbedded with ripple-bedded and cross-bedded sandstone are seen along the mill-race at the mouth of the stream. **Locality 6** (SJ 834829) behind the office of the Museum Trust, reveals a deep fluvial erosion surface. The quarry walls of the interior of the former Engineering Works reveal a normal fault crossing the room at a direction 310°. **Locality 7,** (SJ 835831) Quarrybank House Quarry, shows the same erosion surface and thinning-upwards sets of trough and lenticular planar cross-bedding, whose palaeocurrents are directed to 024°. Abundant rolled ventifacts and mudballs (Bell, 1940) are seen. Most mudballs are red, some green, some zoned with a red exterior and a green interior, others green-red, rare ones red-green-red. It is not known whether this is original or post-depositional colouring (Thompson, *in* Friend, 1966, 291-2). **Please do not hammer or try to extract these balls.**

To study the strata above this cycle, retrace the path to the Office of the Museum Trust and ask for directions in order to cross the river to the Weir (**Locality 8,** SJ 833828). Here *c.* 12m of Mottled Sandstone facies is the equivalent of beds at Frodsham (Frodsham Soft Sandstone Member of the HSF) and one set of cross-strata, which contains deformed and intraset cross-bedding and millet seed lenses is characteristic of the forward parts of a transverse dune. Check that the palaeowind was directed from the northeast. Notice the barite mineralisation. At the south end of this exposure, in the crags above and on the slope to the west of the Mill (SJ 833829), richly micaceous red fine-grained sandstones compare with those at Nether Alderley (Nether Alderley Sandstone Member) (Thompson, 1970a, b). They contain clay galls, lenticular and trough, sometimes deformed, cross-bedding, ripple-bedding, ripple marks, rain-pits and mudcracks belonging to further fluvial cycles. It was here that it is likely that the first reversely magnetised 'Redbeds' were examined (Clegg, *et al.,* 1954). A magnetic dip of -28° upwards was measured, indicating a reversed magnetic field and a palaeolatitude (15°N) for this part of Triassic time. Prove the presence of the Styal Fault (throwing normally *c.* 105m to the west) by walking *c.* 300m along the top of the bank from the weir and examining grey fine-grained dolomitic sandstone and siltstones, red and green mudstones of the Mercia Mudstones high on the river bank (**Locality 9,** SJ 832827) and in the tributary stream (**Locality, 10,** SJ 830827). These beds are thrown against the HSF. Sedimentary structures are comparable with those of **Locality 15** below. Notice the gorge-like nature of the Bollin valley hereabouts; hence the advantage of constructing the weir in 1784.

Return to the Mill and retrace the path to the car park in Styal village (SJ 835835). From there walk southwest into Little Wood. Small outcrops of the Tarporley Siltstone Formation are found in the dry valley (SJ 833833), but study is best confined to the small cycles near the junction of Little and Great Wood (SJ 832831), in the lower parts of Great Wood as far as the second bridge (SJ 832833), and in the north bank of the River Bollin (SJ 831831). The lower parts of the cycles show red medium- to fine-grained cross-bedded or ripple-bedded sandstone with occasional granules and sole structures. The cycles terminate upwards with the interbedding of mudstone and shale with flaggy, ripple-marked siltstone and fine-grained sandstone. Structures to be observed in the siltstones include small-scale trough cross-bedding, convolute bedding, asymmetrical ripple marks of several types, rain-pits, mudcracks, load and flame structure, nodules of gypsum and pseudomorphs after halite. The rapidly interbedded strata have injection structures. Mica is ubiquitous, characteristic and may be indicative of provenance in the distant south, near the Channel (Fitch, *et al.,* 1966, but also see reservations expressed by Taka, 1984). The onset of the mudstones of the first unnamed mudstone formation in the Mercia Mudstone Group is taken where the last substantial sandstone band is found. Malachite may be found on the bedding planes of the MMG in one area (SJ 831832, Figure 14). The mineralisation may be syngenetic but is more likely to be epigenetic and related to the presence of the Styal Fault *c.* 15m to the west. The effect of this fault has caused the mudstones and siltstones of the MMG to become more indurated, broken and contorted, so that they form rapids in the bed of the Bollin, some 60 m to the west of the tributary mouth (**Locality 11,** SJ 831831). From here walk westwards through conifer trees and the meander belt of the Bollin, and examine broken, contorted, fault-affected MMG at **Localities 12** (SJ 830832) and **13** (SJ 829832).

Retrace your steps to the wooden bridge over the Bollin and gain access to the path of the south side of the river. Walk along the rather muddy path westwards, noting exposure of red MMG in the cut banks on the north side of the river (e.g. at SJ 828833), until one reaches the new bridge at Giants Castle Rocks (SJ 827835) where a whole series of exposures may be examined at **Localities 14-19.** Here, in a magnificent river cliff, three rejuvenated tributary valley and two rapids, the Giants Castle 'skerry belt', low in the MMG, are exposed. Succeeding *c.* 11m interbedded red and green shales and siltstones at the base, many larger and smaller cycles of sedimentation are apparent, and are best seen at the foot of the cliff by the pier of the old suspension bridge. Each small cycle comprises an upper division of several centimetres of interbedded green-grey or red dolomitic sandstone (or dolomite).

Structures seen in the upper division include pseudomorphs after halite, injection structures, rain-pits, flat laminae, wave ripple marks, load and flame structures, crinkle marks and mudcracks. Those in the lower division include erosion channels, graded bedding, prod and bounce marks, ?flute casts, intraformational clay galls with imbrication, small-scale cross-strata generated by both unidirectional currents and by wave processes, and marks formed by the wrenching out of salt cubes. Structures developed post-depositionally *in situ* include slumps, load and flame, pseudo-nodules, a sand volcano and geodes occupied by calcite (compare Klein, 1962; Ireland, *et al.*, 1978, Arthurton, 1980). Two cycles at each of two localities **(14 and 15)** have been found to contain *Euestheria minuta* var. *brodieana* (a water flea), and in one cycle there has been identified what may either be the wing of a mayfly (Thompson, 1966a) or a dragonfly (Jarzembowksi, 1989). Trace fossils likely to relate to the activities of animals like water fleas have also been found at **Locality 15.** The gentle Giants Castle anticline can be observed, with its axis running northeast — southwest. Major and minor faults, with accompanying drag, may be seen also, or inferred, at four localities (**16, 17, 18, 19**), the most easterly being the Norcliffe Fault which marks the western extremity of the Norcliffe shatter belt. Additionally, two of the three river terraces of the Bollin can be seen and, near Twinnies Bridge (SJ 838823), the first of these (as well as the sands here at the top of the Giants Castle Rocks) has yielded rolled ventifacts (Thompson & Worsley, 1967). Return to the car parks in Styal village or at Quarrybank Mill by retracing one's steps.

ITINERARY XI

Frodsham area

Ordnance Survey 1:50,000 Sheet 117; 1:25,000 SJ 47/57
British Geological Survey 1:50,000 Sheet 97

The area is reached by car or by taking the Chester train from Manchester to Frodsham. The itinerary, suitable for a half or full day is best accomplished by having papers by McKee (1966, especially figures 6 & 7) and Brookfield (1977) in hand; also that by Thompson (1969).

Route. Ask permission at the Rock Methodist Church (Figure 15) to walk to the back of the building. At **Locality 1,** (SJ 520780) look southwards across the railway cutting to the old quarry and see the core of the Main Dune in the upper parts of the Helsby Sandstone Formation. Note the crest and the brink

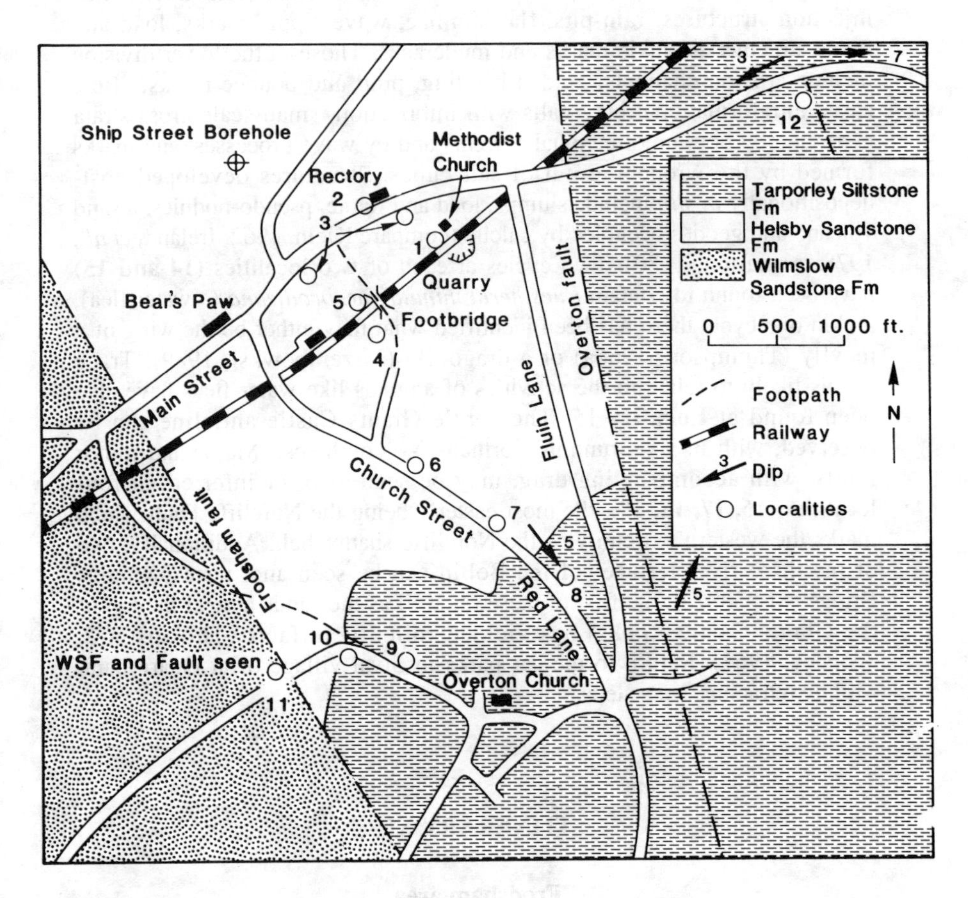

Figure 15. Geological map of the area around Frodsham, Cheshire.

of the dune at its summit. This structure has been interpreted as a transverse dune which was for a time converted into a dome-shaped dune (Thompson, 1969), but also as a transverse draa (very large sand dune) with smaller dunes migrating down its bevelled front (Brookfield, 1977, 1984). Look westwards and establish the presence of a hump-like erosion surface marking the top of the previous dome-shaped dune. Study the types of cross-bedding. Look eastwards and see the northwards-dipping dune above. Regain the road and examine convex-upwards cross beds, which may relate to the northwesterly margins of the Main Dune, in front of the Rectory (**Locality 2,**

SJ 518781). Wind-ripple and grainfall laminae (Hunter, 1977) may be discerned. Walk along the north side of the High Street and the upraised service road on its southern side (**Locality 3**), studying varieties and arrangements of cross-bed sets and intra-sets which are peripheral northwest parts of the Main Dune. Note the major erosion surface which may mark the base of the Main Dune *c.* 50 m west-southwest of the steps. Take the footpath leading south-southeast from the service road to the footbridge (**Locality 4,** SJ 519779), whereupon it is possible to examine the downwind parts of the Main Dune with their gently incline laminae to the east of the bridge and their steeply inclined, straight and convex-upward erosion planes with intervening cross-bedding caused by sand remobilisation to the west of the bridge. Characteristics of dome-shaped and transverse dunes are seen east and west of the bridge respectively. Walk round to the station yard (**Locality 5,** SJ 519779) and go to the end of the former northern platform to study these features further. Wind-ripple, grainfall and occasionally grainflow (i.e. sandflow or avalanche) laminations may be discerned (*cf.* Hunter, 1977). Note the silicification along the joints. Walk up Church Street to **Locality 7,** SJ 521776 (**Locality 6** is in process of being built over) and examine structures of dome-shaped dunes lying immediately below the Tarporley Siltstone Formation at **Locality 8,** (SJ 522775). Walk past Overton Church to Pinmill Brow (**Localities 9, 10,** SJ 518774) where deformed aeolian cross-bedding of a transverse (?) dune is found beneath the TSF. Establish the presence of the Frodsham Fault and the Wilmslow Sandstone Formation *c.* 100m to the west (**Locality 11,** SJ 517774). Return to the main road by Fluin Lane and examine an anticline in typical TSF east of the Overton Fault (**Locality 12,** SJ 526783). Most of the characteristic features of the TSF can be found at **Localities 8, 9** and **12.**

A pleasant afternoon can be spent examining the WSF and Helsby Sandstone Formation on the face of Beacon Hill south of Frodsham (SJ 516770) and west of Five Crosses in the quarry and near the caves (SJ 524761). Alternatively, the type section of the Helsby Sandstone Formation, with intriguing interdigitations of aeolian and fluvial facies in its lower and upper parts and a thick sequence of fluvial facies in its middle part (Delamere Pebbly Sandstone Member), may be examined along the Older Chester Road, Alvanley Lane, in Helsby Quarry and on Helsby Crags (SJ 492754) where mineralised baritic faults and joints are very apparent.

ITINERARIES XII-XIV

Goyt Valley between Marple and Stockport

R. H. Johnson

Ordnance Survey 1:50,000 Sheet 109
British Geological Survey 1:50,000 Sheets 98 & 99 (Drift)

The Lower Goyt Valley offers an opportunity to study some aspects of the stratigraphy of the Late Pleistocene (Devensian) Glacial Stadial and also the history of changing river-channel patterns over the last 10,000 years in the Holocene (Flandrian) epoch.

Although access to the valley sites is possible from many places as there are footpaths throughout the length of the valley, actual site access is often difficult if only one excursion is contemplated. For this reason the map figures include both locality numbers and access points. The itineraries contain lists of localities readily visited from each access point and for convenience the valley is divided into three sections with a general commentary for each part. Locality descriptions are given with each section.

ITINERARY XII

Marple Bridge-Compstall to Marple Aqueduct

Cars can be parked at Marple Bridge, Brabyn's Park car park (SJ 964895) with access to localities 1-5 and at Compstall (SJ 965908) with access to localities 1-5, 6 and 7 (Figure 16).

During the Late Devensian (Dimlington) stadial this area was covered by ice which did not originate in the local Pennine hills, but encroached on to the lower hill slopes from the lowland areas around Manchester. When the ice-sheet began to decay the upper slopes were the first to emerge leaving ice on the lower slopes and in the valley to melt *in situ*. As a consequence, meltwaters were extremely important in eroding new river courses, re-working the glacially transported sediments and also cutting some ice-margin meltwater channels on the flanks of the hillsides. The Goyt Valley downstream of Marple and the Etherow Valley below Compstall show several interesting geomorphological features resulting from such conditions and also a number of localities where the glacial and fluvial sediments can be seen overlying Palaeozoic and Mesozoic rocks.

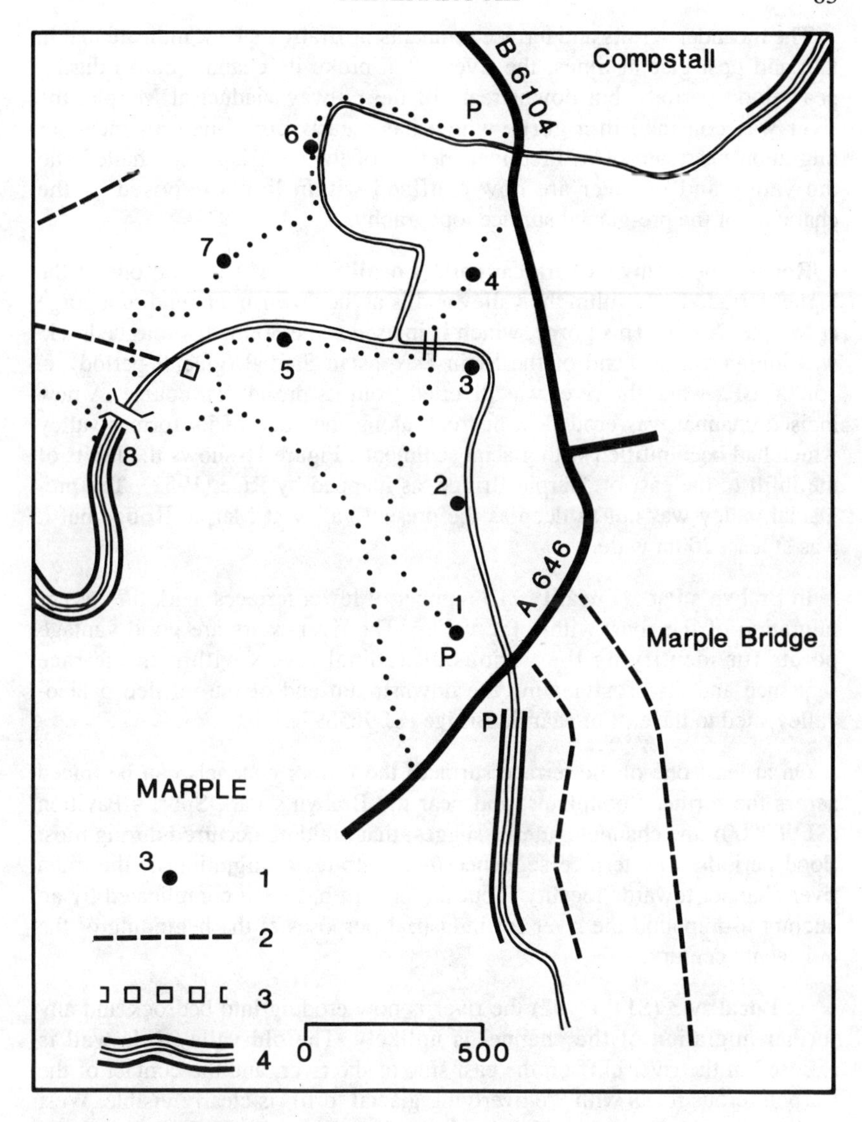

Figure 16. Geomorphological features in the Marple Bridge area.
P. Car Parking facility. Key in bottom left refers to:
1. Locality number.
2. Former valley section now infilled with glacial deposits.
3. Abandoned valley meander eroded in Carboniferous rocks.
4. Present river course incised into underlying Palaeozoic strata..
Scale in metres.

The meander scrolls and terrace remnants of Brabyn's Park indicate that in late and post-glacial times, the river often broke its channel banks during peak flood periods, but downstream of the railway viaduct at Marple, the river was confined in a gorge which has clearly controlled all meander migration upstream of it. Free meandering of the river has been halted and the valley and its river are now confined within limits imposed by the character of the pre-glacial surface topography.

Route. The Brabyn's Park car park (**Locality 1**) is situated on one of the higher terrace-flats within the valley and is at the downstream end of a gorge at Marple Bridge. This gorge, which is incised some 30 metres into bedrock, was initiated at the end of the Main Devensian Stadial (glacial period), c. 15,000 BP., when the river was diverted from its pre-glacial course. A new incised channel was eroded in bedrock along the edge of its former valley which had been infilled with glacial sediments. Figure 16 shows the limits of the infill to the east of Marple Bridge, as mapped by Rice (1957). The pre-glacial valley was not as deep as the present valley at Marple Bridge but it was at least 200m wide.

In Brabyn's Park (**Locality 2**) a number of lower terraces mark the former migration of the river within the valley. The river weirs are good vantage points for identifying the various altitudinal levels within the terrace sequence and also for viewing the downstream end of the infilled palaeo-valley sited to the east of Marple Bridge (SJ 965897).

On at least one of the terrace surfaces the former channels can be traced across the former floodplains, and near the Brabyn's Park Sport's Pavilion (SJ 962900), the channel patterns suggest that braiding occurred during most flood periods. The terrace sequence demonstrates a migration of the main river channel towards locality 3 but the pattern has been complicated by an attempt to impound the river for industrial purposes at the beginning of the nineteenth century.

At **Locality 3** (SJ 967902) the river is now eroding into bedrock and any further migration of the channel is unlikely. The old valley side-wall is exposed in the river cliff on the east side of the river, and the contact of the Carboniferous rocks with the overlying glacial 'drift' is clearly visible. West of the river, the bedrock surface occurs only a few metres below the terrace surfaces its position having been proved in the old Ludworth colliery which here extended both under the river and the present floodplain.

The upper and more extensive terraces in Brabyn's Park probably date from the late-glacial and early post-glacial periods (Johnson, 1989). Resistivity traverses undertaken in this part of the Park have shown that the terraces are formed of sands and silts 1.5m thick that overlie coarse gravel beds over 3m thick. At the outer limit of the river bend two low terraces mark the most recent stages in the river's downcutting. The lowest, which is very limited in its distribution and no more than two metres above the channel bed, is probably only one hundred and fifty years old and its formation reflects the changes resulting from the Agricultural and the Industrial Revolutions; the higher feature probably dates from the time when the land was first deforested — an event which probably took place during the late Mesolithic and early Neolithic Periods (c. 10,000-4,000 yrs. BP).

A bridle road at **Locality 4** leads from the Park Bridge (dated 1813) to Compstall. A suite of terraces, similar to those in Brabyn's Park, occur upstream of the Etherow-Goyt confluence and there are two higher terrace remnants to the east of the lane.

At the eastern end of Brabyn's Park (**Locality 5**) (SJ 960903) river downcutting has now exposed sandstone beds in the floor of the present river channel. At this point, the modern river course cuts across the line of the former pre-glacial valley (Figure 16) and the exposure demonstrates that the pre-glacial valley-floor was not eroded to any depth beyond that at which the present river is now downcutting.

The changes in channel pattern as seen from localities 2-7 reveal the extent to which the river has freely migrated across the valley-floor. Eroded in a sector once filled with glacial drift the modern valley topography is gradually reverting to a form determined by the bedrock surface, but various relic features remain to show the extent of the glacial modification. To the south of the river, a deep embayment (SJ 967901) has been cut into the valley flank during the course of the valley incision. In it there is an abandoned stream flood course now covered by alder and other scrub woodland. Close by, on the highest terrace, there is a meander cut-off whose core (SJ 959901) forms the highest part of the valley-floor in this part of the Park. These features can be viewed from the path which leads up to the canal tow-path from locality 5.

Access to the areas downstream of Brabyn's Park is possible by following the path leading to the Canal tow-path (**Locality 6**). The path from Compstall is along the west bank of the Etherow and through Redbrow Wood. Good views of the terraces are possible from the path and it is possible to identify similar terrace stages to those found in Brabyn's Park. The Redbrow Wood slopes have been much affected by slippage but, in the gullies, drift sections shows gravel beds and sand overlying till. The sections occur within the pre-glacial stadial. The erratic content and lithological composition of the gravels has been compared with those occuring in downstream glacial and terrace deposits and appear statistically to be derived from the same general set of deposits (Johnson, 1989).

Downstream of the wood, the path continues across the terraces to Lower Watersmeet Farm where an old coal tip covers part of the valley side (**Locality 7**). It then continues upslope along the farm road leading to Romiley. Two hundred metres from the farm (SJ 995905) a path leads back down the slope to pass under the rail bridge and canal aqueduct (SJ 955902). Immediately west of the latter, the path continues upslope again to join the canal tow-path.

ITINERARY XIII

Marple Aqueduct to Chadkirk

Car Parks are at (i) Marple Bridge, Brabyn's Park car park. (SJ 964895), with a walk to the Aqueduct along the Canal tow-path and access to 8 and 9; (ii) at Nabtop, Marple (SJ 952894), with restricted parking and access to localities 9 & 11; (iii) Marple Hall (SJ 945894) with restricted parking and access to localities 9 and 12; and at (iv) Chadkirk Farm Trail car park (SJ 937896) with access to localities 8,9; 9,10; 9,11. (Figure 17).

Access to this part of the valley is somewhat restricted as it is only possible to cross the river at Chadkirk and at the Canal Aqueduct. Some localities on the south side can be visited by using the farm road to Marple Dale and local footpaths near Marple Hall School, but they do not provide a continuous route along the valley-floor. The route on the north side is continuous from the Aqueduct providing the tow-path to the west end of the Hydebank Canal Tunnel is followed. The return to the main valley at Chadkirk is then made by taking the footpath through Kirk Wood to locality 10.

Route. The Aqueduct (**Locality 8**) is sited at the upstream end of the Ley Hey Park river gorge which is a large incised valley-meander eroded in Carboniferous sandstones and mudrocks. Public access to the gorge unfortunately is very restricted, but the aqueduct does provide a good viewpoint for examining the dramatic contrast in the valley cross-sections upstream and downstream. To the east, the rivers have developed wide, open valleys by removing the glacial infill, but to the west, the river is now deeply incised within an entrenched valley-meander. Rice (1957) has suggested that,

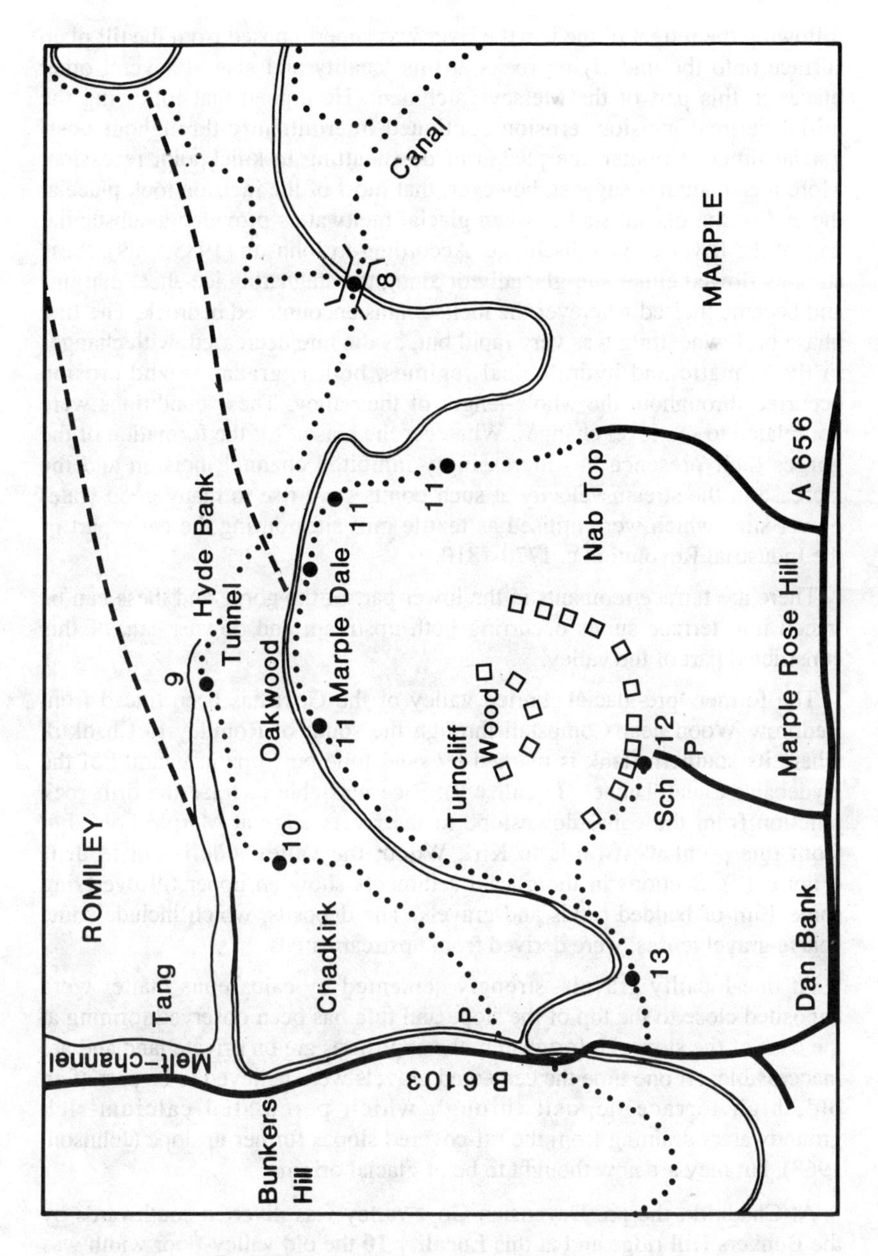

Figure 17. Geomorphological features in the Marple – Chadkirk Area (key as in Figure 16).

following the retreat of the ice, the river was superimposed from the till plain surface onto the underlying rocks at this locality and also at several other places in this part of the Mersey catchment. He argued that following the initial vertical incision, erosion continued intermittently throughout post-glacial times attributed the phases of downcutting to knickpoint recession. More recent studies suggest, however, that most of the incision took place at the end of the glacial stadial when glacial meltwaters provided a substantial part of the River Goyt's discharge. According to Johnson (1985,1989), these streams flowed either sub-glacially or along the stagnating ice-sheet margins and became incised wherever the meltstreams encountered bedrock. The first phase of downcutting was very rapid but, as the rate decreased, with changes in the climatic and hydrological regimes, both aggradation and erosion occurred throughout the whole length of the valley. These conditions were not related to sea-level changes. Whatever the reason for the formation of the gorges their presence has increasingly inhibited channel incision and the increase in the stream velocity at such points gave rise to many good water power sites which were utilised as textile mill sites during the early part of the Industrial Revolution c. 1770-1810.

There are terrace remnants in the lower part of the gorge and these can be traced into terrace suites occurring both upstream and downstream of this constricted part of the valley.

The former 'pre-glacial' buried valley of the Goyt has been traced from Redbrow Wood near Compstall through the south of Romiley to Chadkirk where its southern flank is marked by sandstone outcrops in vicinity of the Hydebank Canal Tunnel (**Locality 9**). Rice was able to trace the drift-rock junction from the canal downslope to the rivers edge at Marple Fold, but from this point westwards to Kirk Wood, the valley-side is cut in drift (Figure 17). Sections in the glacial sediments show an upper till overlying some 15m of bedded sands and gravels. The deposits, which include some coarse gravel lenses, were derived from upstream areas.

At one locality gravels, strongly cemented by calcareous matter were deposited close to the top of the slope and tufa has been observed forming at the base of the slope. Unfortunately the exposures are on private land and are inaccessible. At one time the cemented gravels were believed to be part of an old, high terrace deposit through which percolated calcium-rich groundwaters draining from the till-covered slopes further upslope (Johnson, 1968), but they are now thought to be of glacial origin.

At Chadkirk, the pre-Devensian Goyt valley was diverted southwards by the Bunkers Hill ridge and at this **Locality 10** the old valley-floor width was at least 400m wide. Borehole evidence indicates that the rock floor is only 5m below present the floodplain.

A large meltwater channel was eroded to the west of Romiley and along the western flank of Werneth Low between Tang and Woodley (Figure 17). Although its floor at Tang is now some 18m above the present Goyt Valley floor, its meltstream was undoubtedly very active at the end of the last glacial period, when water was diverted from the Upper Tame Valley and may have caused the Goyt river to shift its course southwards before becoming incised into the underlying bedrock.

At Chadkirk, the Chadkirk Farm Trail is located on an extensive terrace which covers most of the valley-floor. On its surface there is evidence for many former flood-channels.

The farm road and public footpath leading to Marple Dale from Marple provides several viewpoints where the lower part of the Ley Hey gorge and the terraces within it are visible (**Locality 11**). The river is now deeply entrenched in bedrock and its entrenchment continues downstream from the gorge to Lower Dale Farm (SJ 945902). The channel is now 2-3m below the valley-floor and is confined along the north side of the Dale, but its migration across the valley-floor in former times can be studied from the pattern of terraces present to the south of the river. The terrace spreads are now covered by a veneer of alluvium but trial pits and resistivity surveys showed that much of the valley-floor aggradation is of gravel material. Up to the time when the upper terraces were formed, the river flowed through the now abandoned valley-meander south of Turncliff Wood (Figure 17) and its migration between two entrenched valley-meanders was restricted. Where the valley-sides were formed of glacial material however, undercutting was possible and the river channel became increasingly more sinuous as the valley infill was removed. Detailed mapping (Johnson 1989), has shown that the later stages of the migration were influenced by the construction of point bars which caused the river to shift northwards into its present alignment.

The footpath to Chadkirk follows along the south side of the river and passes through the water-gap formed when the river was diverted. The change in river direction and the abandonment of the former course is considered below.

The abandoned valley meander is visible from the top path along the edge of the school playing fields (**Locality 12**). On the path, glacial gravels are exposed overlying a thin till formation which itself caps high sandstone cliffs. Some paths lead to the base of the cliffs and these can be used to examine the features in the valley meander core.

The abandoned valley-meander is asymmetrical in cross-section and within it two high terrace remnants have been preserved. They occur on the inner side of the meander and slope steeply in the general downstream direction. Their steep gradient is probably explained by their location within a rock gorge which separated two drift-filled valley sections. The terraces, unlike those in Marple Dale, contain only thin gravel lenses and trial pits revealed sand thicknesses varying between 2.5 and 3m (Johnson, 1989). The gravels are similar in their stone content to that found in the other terraces, but the comparative absence of coarse sediments suggests that they were deposited in slack water on the inner bend of a meander, where the river was actively undercutting along its outer margin.

Several factors may have contributed to the relatively recent river diversion in this part of the valley. Initially, a spur extended southwards from the north side across the line of the present valley and was formed of glacial sediments, except where the isolated rock feature at Turncliff Wood formed its southern tip. The shifts and distortion of the river course at the upper end of the now abandoned gorge helped to erode the spur, especially on its eastern flank where the glacial sediments were more susceptible to river under-cutting, spring sapping and slope slippage. Spring sapping and headward erosion would also occur on the spur's western wall especially at the junction between the bedrock and the drift. A small tributary stream probably cut back following the line of the present river course from Oakwood to Chadkirk Mill, but any actual derangement was delayed until the erosional processes, including seepage and slumping, had reduced the spur width and allowed first groundwater springs, and then floodwaters, to form a passage through the neck of a meander. The diversion would result in a steepening and truncation of the valley-floor profile so that eventually all river flood-waters would be diverted. A new river course would be quickly established cutting across the spur and the glacial sediments on the sides of the valley would also have been rapidly eroded to produce the present valley topography.

At the downstream end of the abandoned valley meander and opposite Chadkirk Mill, the footpath crosses a small gully in which glacial sediments and terrace gravels are exposed (**Locality 13**) (SJ 941897). At their base the gravels overlie sandstones in which the river is now entrenched. The gully section shows some 3m of river terrace gravels which are strongly imbricated, cross-bedded and formed of well-rounded pebbles. At the back of the terrace, glacial deposits are exposed in the gully which are part of the Stockport Formation the principal component in the Devensian stratigraphic succession. It consists of a basal till overlain by fluvioglacial sands and gravels in which are interbedded thin tills, laminated clays and silts which are themselves overlain by a higher till member. Such a depositional sequence frequently leads to slumping on the valley-sides and the sequence of deposits varies greatly from place to place, but exposures of the same formation are visible along the flanks of the Marple Brook valley to Dan Bank and it is generally present throughout the area from Stockport to Hyde (Simpson, 1959; Johnson, 1985).

ITINERARY XIV

Chadkirk to Stockport

Cars can be parked at Chadkirk Farm Trail car park (SJ 937896) with access to localities 14-15, and at Poise Brook, Offerton (SJ 936889) with restricted car parking and access to localities 14-18. There is also parking at Stockport Little Moor, Woodbank Park car park (SJ 910900) with access to localities 13-18 and restricted parking at Stockport Museum, Vernon Park (SJ 909908) for access to localities 13-18. The Goyt footpath from Chadkirk is along the north side of the valley to the Higher and Lower Waterside farms and then continues close to the river to a new bridge opposite the Poise Brook confluence. (Figure 18). Although it is possible to go to Bredbury using the farm roads to Goyt and Middle Farms on the north side of the river, the preferred route is to cross the bridge and continue along the south side of the Goyt to the Woodbank and Vernon Parks in Offerton and East Stockport.

At Chadkirk Mill, the Goyt leaves the west Pennine Upland margin where the valley is eroded in Carboniferous rocks with the lower slopes mantled with surficial glacial materials, and enters the lowland zone of northwest England. Here, the rivers have become incised into a till plain and their valleys sides are formed of glacial deposits which are stratigraphically part of the Stockport Formation. At the base there are tills which are overlain by thick sands and gravels, interbedded tills, laminated clays and then by a higher till member. The whole succession was formed during the Devensian/Dimlington Stadial and reflects changing depositional conditions as the ice stagnated at the hill margin (Johnson, 1985). Although sections are affected by slumping, a tripartite sequence of deposits has been mapped on the valley sides for much of this section (Simpson, 1959), but this is an over-simplification as sections exposed during the construction of the M63 motorway at Bredbury (SJ 918920) showed that the basal till was overlain by a sequence of en-glacial and melt-out tills separated by fluvioglacial sands and gravels. At least four till members are present in this part of the valley-infill succession.

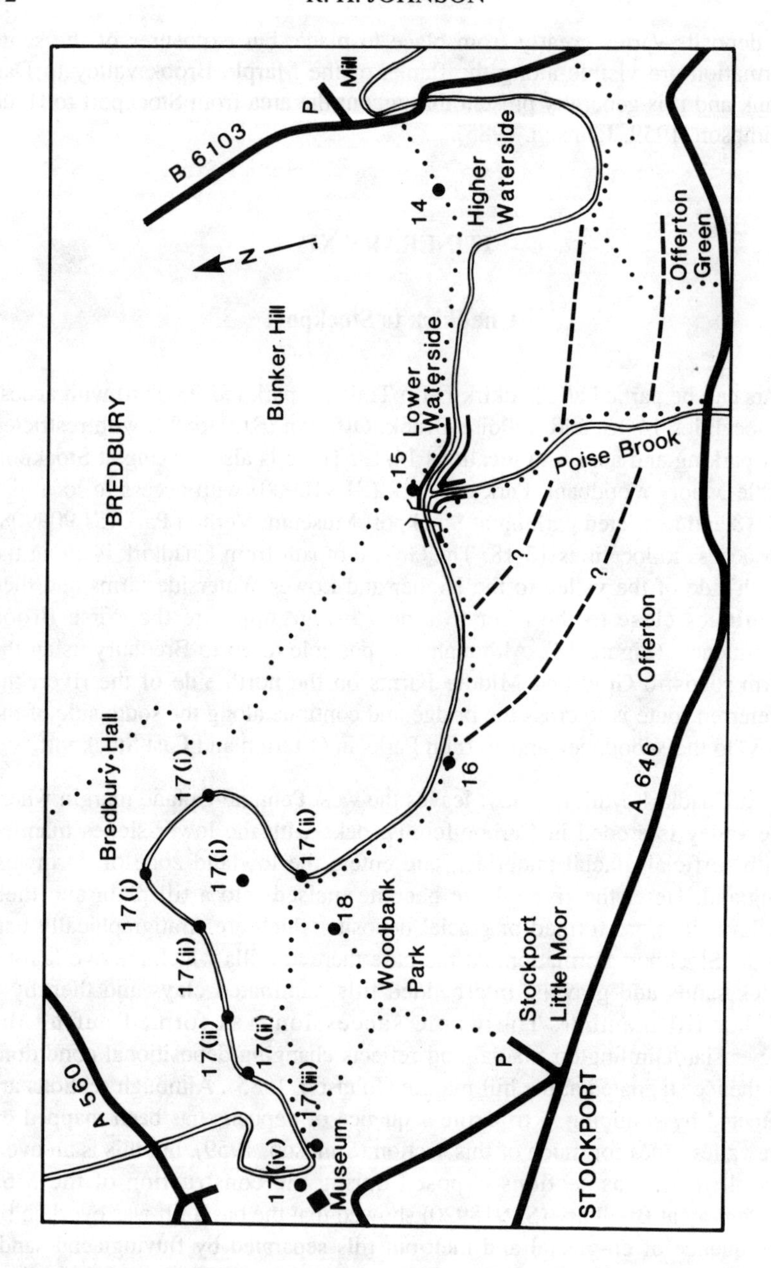

Figure 18. Geomorphological features in the Offerton-East Stockport Area (key as in Figure 16).

For most of its length, the river Goyt has been free to meander incising itself into these glacial sediments, but the underlying bedrock surface is now exposed in the channel at several places. Wherever this occurs the river becomes confined within its channel course and its ability to meander has become increasingly restricted.

In this lowland zone the topography of the bedrock surface beneath the glacial sediments is very irregular. Some of the more resistant rocks probably form ridges beneath the till and the weaker rock belts may well have influenced the alignments of the pre-glacial drainage pattern. From Chadkirk westwards the Goyt was originally aligned along the strike of the Permian Collyhurst Sandstones, a formation of weak, uncemented sandstones with mudstones. The former valley can be traced through Lower Bredbury (SJ 918912) into the Tame Valley at Brinnington and then northwestwards through Reddish North where a north-south escarpment lies buried beneath a glacial overburden (Simpson, 1959). The escarpment formed by sandstones of the Sherwood Sandstone Group (Triassic) has a crest line at c. 60m O.D. and stands above the deep palaeovalley to the east. The diversion of the river through Stockport, where the sandstone rocks are exposed (SJ 896907), occured in late Pleistocene times, but how it took place is unknown although it is probable that the former valley was greatly modified by the effects of both ice-sheet erosion and deposition. Considerable overdeepening has occurred in some places. For example, at the Old Bredbury colliery (SJ 919925), the valley infill is 45m thick and the bedrock surface is at 42.6m O.D. (Taylor, 1963).

Route. Higher and Lower Waterside Farms (**Locality 14**). Note that this part of the valley is accessible from either Chadkirk or Offerton Green but there is no link with other paths mentioned in this itinerary.

These farmsteads are located on a suite of broad extensive terrace surfaces which reveal a history of river channel pattern changes upstream of the Poise Brook – Goyt confluence. Originally, two large valley-meanders were eroded at Chadkirk. In the upper meander, the bend was sited to the north of the Chadkirk Mill works, but the river was forced southwards by the Bunkers Hill escarpment (SJ 935900) and an extensive embayment was eroded on the south side of the valley at Offerton Green (SJ 934888). An abandoned meander channel lies beneath the old river cliff, which has been affected by slumping. Although no pre-Pleistocene rocks are exposed, Rice believed that the embayment was eroded within the infill of a former valley course.

Along the Offerton Gorge (**Locality 15**). The evidence for the supposed river derangement occurs in the vicinity of the Poise Brook confluence with the Goyt. This confluence lies within the Red Rock Fault-zone where Lower

Coal Measures are exposed on the eastern side of the fault and Lower Permian Collyhurst Sandstones to the west. In the lower Poise Brook valley there are several exposures of these strata but their relationship to each other has been disputed since it may be explained in terms of either faulting or as an unconformity.

It has been argued by Rice that a buried valley is located in the upper part of the Poise Brook valley (Figure 18) and that the present river course is along a diversionary route. The evidence for such a buried valley, however, is inconclusive for although the bedrock surface rises to the south of the present river gorge it is very irregular and there are no outcrops of Carboniferous or Permo-Triassic rocks in the upper parts of the Poise Brook clough, or indeed in the area south of the Stockport-Marple road, which might indicate the southern edge to Rice's postulated buried valley. It is therefore suggested that the valley constriction in the present valley resulted not from a river derangement, but from superimposition during downcutting.

The evidence for this superimposition is found at the gorge itself and on the north side of the river. From Higher Waterside Farm (SJ 934896) the northern flank of the valley is relatively steep-sided, straight and its alignment is NW-SE. Downstream of Lower Waterside Farm (SJ 928896) the higher terraces become quite extensive but at Poise Brook a terrace edge actually lies above the lip of the gorge, which is only incised to a depth of 5m. There is much less constriction in the width of the valley at this point than occurs in the other gorge sections further upstream. Also, the incision into bedrock did not occur until after the terrace aggradation had taken place – a condition not found at any other gorge.

At the Offerton Cricket ground (**Location 16**) (SJ 925896) and downstream from the Poise Brook – Goyt confluence there is a path on the south side of the river which follows the underlying bedrock. Here, the slope is buttressed at its base by outcrops of sandstone, but there has been much slumping of the slope, especially where sands and gravels outcrop on the middle slopes. At the top of the slope a till bed forms a steep landslide cliff or 'scar'.

The cricket ground is located on a river terrace within a small embayment. This embayment, Rice suggested, is the downstream end of the infilled, buried valley-section. However, the Collyhurst Sandstone exposures which supposedly mark the valley-infill edges occur only a few metres above river level and unlike any of the other buried valley infills this one would have been severely restricted in width.

The Woodbank and Vernon Parks (**Location 17**) exhibit geological features which have been described by Broadhurst (1982), and his account provides several features of interest:

(i) The river channel is now confined within the valley in a series of meander bends. At its outer margins the channel edges are confined in bedrock, but the past shifts in the river channel can be traced from the pattern of the terrace levels within the meander cores.

The highest terrace has an upper and lower element and these can be traced into areas west of Stockport where they form the Mersey High Terrace (Jones, 1924). This terrace aggradation began to form in late-glacial and continued to develop throughout early post-glacial (Flandrian) times. Initially the aggradation was formed by meltwaters which re-distributed the glacial debris in a number of braided channels, but later changes were determined by discharge fluctuations resulting from climatic change (Johnson, 1985, 1989). Such conditions were also complicated by a rapid, concurrent, but not necessarily continuous rise in sea-level.

(ii) Exposures of Collyhurst Sandstone and terrace gravels in the river banks are to be found around the edge of this large meander. The sandstones are poorly cemented by iron oxides. They were formed in an arid inland basin environment by aeolian and ephemeral fluvial processes.

(iii) Outcrops of Collyhurst Sandstone are exposed in the river bank. Immediately upstream of the weir there is a gravel bank in the river which contains flat and disc-shaped pebbles that show a strong, imbrication. The deposited pebbles include glacial erratics, local sandstones and also some formed from old bricks!

(iv) Weathering of limestone and gypsum boulders may be observed close to the path leading from the Museum to the river edge.

(v) Two large erratic boulders (volcanic tuffs from the Lake District) are located close to the museum; there is also an Eskdale granite boulder at the bottom of the slope.

ITINERARY XV

The Mineralisation of Ecton Hill, Staffordshire

R. S. W. Braithwaite

Ordnance Survey 1:50,000 Sheet 119;
1:25,000 Outdoor Leisure Map The White Peak
British Geological Survey 1:50,000 Sheet 111

Ecton Hill (centred on SK 100580) in the parish of Wetton, Staffordshire, is a prominent feature on the east side of the scenic Manifold valley. It is of hog's back form, rising to 369m (1212 ft.) near its northern end, sloping steeply to the Manifold on its northern and western flanks, and more gently on its eastern side to a narrow cul-de-sac road at Back of Ecton. The Leek and Manifold Valley Light Railway ran along the river bank at its base, but has now been converted to a walking track.

The Hulme End to Wetton road also follows the line of the river, and the best access to the hill is by this road from Hulme End or, from the north, via Longnor by a narrow road branching east off the B5053 just before Warslow. From the south it is best reached from the A52, turning north into the B5053 at the Bottom House crossroads 5 km (3ml) NW of Waterhouses.

Geology. Ecton Hill is on the southwest edge of the Carboniferous Limestone outcrop of the Derbyshire Dome, where the contorted limestones dip under the Millstone Grit. The mineralised part of the hill is of Lower Carboniferous (Viséan, D1) limestones, the upper parts of which (Brigantian, D2) are dark, muddy and shaly. The Upper Carboniferous (Namurian) rocks are apparently unconformable, exposures of the junction being poor, and are shaly in the lower portions, but pass up into thick sandstones. Small Viséan limestone inliers outcrop to the west nearby at Butterton, and 5 km away just north of Mixon where, interestingly, rather similar mineralisation is found. East-west compression has folded the limestones into a fractured anticlinorium, with a regional plunge of some 10° to the NW (Critchley, 1979). The fracturing is predominantly north-south and in the areas of most intense folding gave access to mineralising solutions.

Mineralisation. The mineralisation of the Derbyshire Dome is concentrated in the upper parts of the Carboniferous Limestone, where it abuts against the impermeable cap of the shales. Normally this mineralisation consists of primary sulphides of lead and subsidiary zinc, in a gangue whose predominant species are zoned according to temperature of formation in increasing order calcite, baryte (barite) and fluorite. Other elements are rare and limited in occurrence, for example traces of nickel and mercury are found in the fluorite zone on the eastern margin and, more importantly, copper is found, also in the fluorite zone, mostly along the eastern and south eastern margins of the outcrop.

The mineralisation of Ecton Hill is an exception to this general pattern in that copper is the predominant ore metal in a small area of concentrated mineralisation. Immediately adjacent across the river to the northwest, Dale Mine is of "normal" lead-predominant mineralisation, and most other mines in the vicinity are also normal, such as those at Wettonmill 2 km to the south, and the concentrated vein-complex at Highfields Mine 5 km to the south-southeast.

Other small but significant concentrations of copper mineralisation do occur nearby, and have been mined in the inlier at Mixon, at Ribden 11 km to the south, and mixed with lead and zinc in the Snelston inlier 6km SSW of Ashbourne, south of the main limestone outcrop. Are there buried copper deposits, for example between Ecton and Mixon?

Another feature characteristic of the Ecton Hill deposits is that the main economic copper deposits were found in large near-vertical pipes, uncommon in the rest of the area, where vein deposits predominate. These pipes are found in the northern parts of the hill, in the region of most intense fracturing, closely associated with mineral veins along north-south fractures, with some east-west cross-veins and minor bedding-plane replacement deposits along fold axes. The textures of the pipe and vein deposits suggest cavity-filling deposition.

Mineralogy. The gangue minerals in the Ecton Hill deposits are the three "Derbyshire" gangue minerals fluorite, calcite and baryte. Ecton Hill is clearly in the fluorite zone. The fluorite invariably forms cubes, not usually large, 1 cm across being exceptional. These are normally colourless, but sometimes purple of "Blue John" colouration type, and are never fluorescent in ultraviolet light. Pyritic inclusions, usually chalcopyrite, are common in the fluorite. The calcite is usually off-white cleavable massive, with little transparency, but in cavities crystallises mainly as colourless and fairly clear scalenohedra. The crystals from large cavities in the pipes occasionally reached 10 cm or more in length, and were often richly sprinkled with small sharp chalcopyrite crystals, on the surfaces and as inclusions. Unfortunately, not many of these magnificent specimens have been preserved in museums, but fragments of such crystals can still be found on the river bank and on dumps, especially those associated with Ecton Deep level. The baryte is massive, and of cockscomb habit into cavities, opaque and usually off-white to pinkish-white. One small lens in shaly matrix in the Waterbank section of Clayton adit, at the southern end of the mineralised area, consisted of pinkish calcite, colourless fluorite, and beautiful pale blue crystals of the strontium sulphate celestine (Braithwaite, Greenland Ryback, 1963; Braithwaite, 1983), with a little golden acicular millerite (NiS) (Starkey, 1983). Pitchy bituminous material is not uncommon, in small quantities, throughout the area.

The main copper ore mineral is chalcopyrite ($CuFeS_2$), massive in bulk, such as in the pipes, but in small sharp crystals when growing free into spaces, as cavity linings, or when sprinkling the surfaces of gangue mineral crystals or when found as inclusions within them. Other copper sulphides reported are bornite (Cu_5FeS_4) and chalcocite (Cu_2S) (Ford & Serjeant, 1964). The primary lead and zinc ores are galena (PbS) and sphalerite (ZnS) respectively. Traces of the nickel sulphide millerite, have been mentioned above.

The Ecton mines are notable for their wide range of secondary minerals, often colourful and attractive, formed by the oxidation of the primary sulphides in the oxidation zone above the water table. The iron in the copper sulphides forms red-brown oxides and rusty stains. Lead secondary minerals are uncommon at Ecton, but zinc forms a number of species. These include smithsonite ($ZnCO_3$) as crumbly "dry-bone ore" and occasionally as small rounded crystals; hemimorphite ($Zn_4Si_2O_7(OH)_2.H_2O$) rarely as crusts of colourless blades, and hydrozincite ($Zn_5(CO_3)_2(OH)_6$) as white stalactitic crusts, sometimes streaked with green (Braithwaite, Ryback & Greenland, 1963). Zinc shares with copper in forming the delicate pale blue-green feathery crusts of aurichalcite ($(Zn,Cu)_5(CO_3)_2(OH)_6$), and darker green rounded blobs of rosasite ($(Cu,Zn)_2CO_3(OH)_2$), related to malachite. The delicate sky-blue blades and needles of serpierite ($Ca(Cu,Zn)_4(SO_4)_2(OH)_6.3H_2O$) are a rarity (Braithwaite & Knight, 1968; Braithwaite, 1983). Other secondary minerals reported from Ecton include the ruby-red cuprite (Cu_2O) (Serjeant, 1956b), black tenorite (Cu_20) (Serjeant, 1957), deep blue azurite ($Cu_3(CO_3)_2(OH)_2$) (Adam, 1848), and the commonest of all, the bright green malachite ($Cu_3(CO_3)_2(OH)_2$), sometimes confused with the amorphous green silicate chrysocolla. The water-soluble blue chalcanthite ($CuSO_4.5H_2O$) may crystallise underground, but is hardly likely to persist on the dumps. Linarite, containing both lead and copper ($PbCuSO_4(OH)_2$) is found, very rarely, as beautiful little bright royal-blue blades (Braithwaite, 1983), somewhat less dark coloured than the azurite.

Mining History. The early history of mining in the area is unknown, but serious mining was in hand during the 17th Century when gunpowder was used in mining for the first time in Britain at Ecton copper mine. The peak period of production was in the 18th Century, when Ecton mines were the richest copper mines in Britain, demand being high for copper-bottoming ships. The richest deposits in the pipes were soon exhausted, however, and Parys mine in Anglesey took over as Britain's prime producer. Production at Ecton was intermittent in the 19th Century, and had ceased altogether by 1890. For further information see Robey & Porter, 1972.

Mining methods. Mining at Ecton took place almost entirely underground, access to the workings being mostly by railed horizontal adit levels, very convenient with the deposits being in a hill, and also by shafts, particularly essential for working the deeper deposits below river level. These lower parts, being below the water table, had to be drained by pumping to the adit levels, which by themselves could only lower the water table to just above river level. Pumping is a major expense in deep mines and if stopped, even for a short period, serious flooding can result and is very difficult to reverse.

The mines. The positions of the main named mines are shown on Figure 19. Most surface shafts are now blocked, but some remain open, **so great care must be taken to avoid falling down them, and to avoid throwing stones or anything else down them** – people might be visiting the underground workings! Some adit levels are still accessible with appropriate permission (see later) by suitably equipped and accompanied parties, and the great open emptied pipe workings can still be seen. The two largest pipes outcrop at Deep Ecton shaft and Clayton shaft respectively.

Routes. On approaching Ecton from the direction of Warslow a spectacular view of Ecton Hill emerges near SK 094585 as the road slopes steeply down to the Manifold valley. Note the "hog's back" topography, and the prominent large dumps of Dutchman Mine straight ahead, about halfway up the hillside. Below these dumps note the recent reafforestation of old dressing-floor dumps. To the left of the dumps note the Castle Folly, Ecton House, and above this the line of the wall and small old farm buildings running straight up the hill and ending near the top in a cluster of buildings which mark the approximate position of the outcrop of Ecton Pipe. Dale Mine level is to the left of the road at the bottom of the hill, among the bushes near the river bank (SK 095585).

Cross the river and turn right, to find limited car parking space beside the road near where it bends to the right. From here one can explore up the hill directly, or walk along the road round the northern end of the hill, noting the outcrops of contorted limestone with some very curious structures, some of which are due to slump phenomena. Troughs or "synclines" in the form of angular intersections are particularly difficult to interpret. Passing the site of the large Apes Tor adit, turn right along the lane to Back of Ecton.

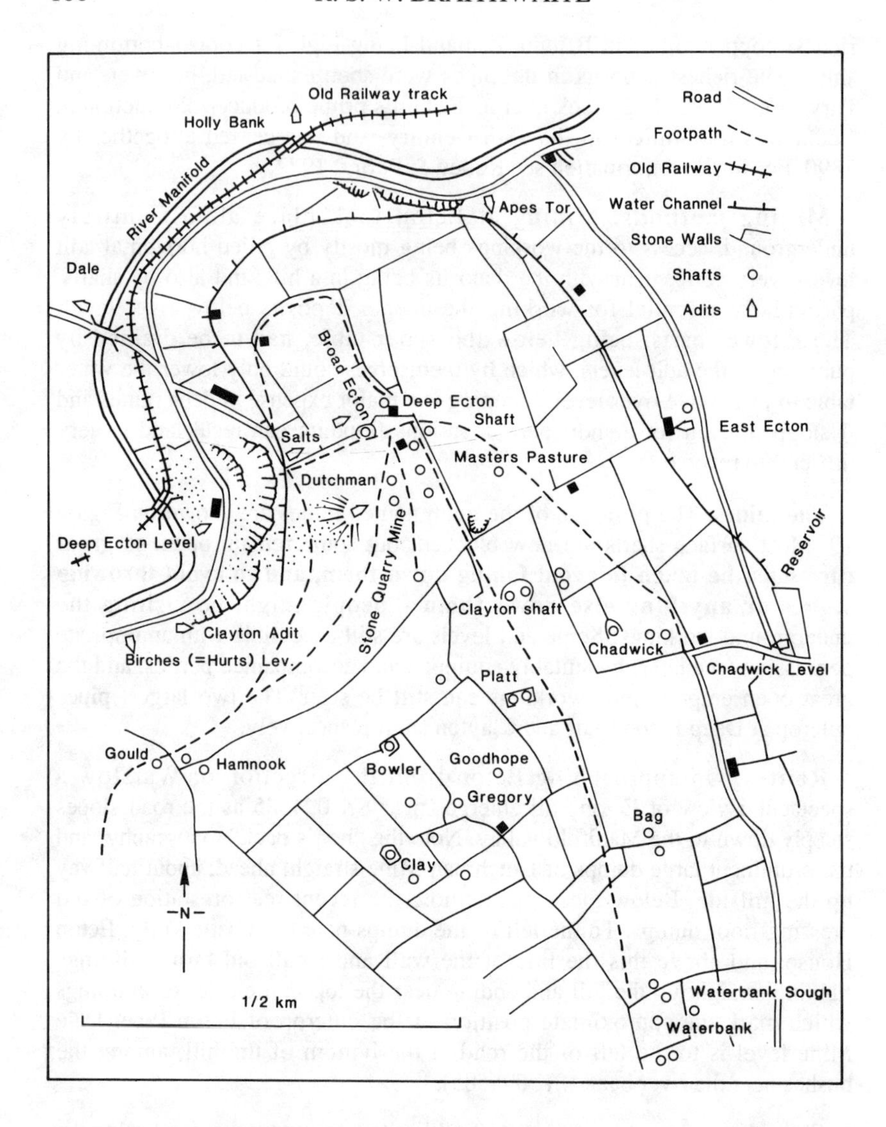

Figure 19. Map of Ecton Hill, showing the distribution of mines.

For a shorter itinerary leave the road at Chadwick Mine (SK 103581) at the top of the zig-zag of the road and explore to the top of, and over the hill from here, but for a better but longer itinerary proceed a little further south and start the exploration from Waterbank Mine, from which Bag Mine, Goodhope Mine and the other mine dumps in their vicinity are easily reached. From these dumps all the common ore and gangue minerals of the area may be collected, and with a little luck, the rare serpierite and linarite.

Trend northwards, towards the top of the hill, past the site of the outcrop of Clayton Pipe, near SK 101581, to the site of the outcrop of Ecton Pipe at the junction of the tracks at around SK 099584. Small, scattered, partly grassed-over dumps in the fields around here are good collecting grounds for the usual minerals, and in particular for malachite and azurite. From here it is not far to the road and car parking below.

Exploration of the underground workings is well worthwhile, but only for properly equipped and led parties. Birches level, by the road, has little of interest, but Clayton level and Salts level give access to fascinating old workings. Enquiries should be made to Mr. G. Cox, at Ecton House, for possibilities of arranging organised visits to these workings.

Permission to visit the different parts of the hill should be obtained from Mr. G. Cox at Ecton House, and from the relevant farmhouses on the eastern side of the hill.

ITINERARY XVI

Building Stones of Manchester City Centre

I. M. Simpson and F. M. Broadhurst

Since the publication in 1975 of *A Building Stones Guide to Central Manchester* by Simpson and Broadhurst numerous developments have taken place in the city. Most of the original guide is still useful but this excursion provides an opportunity to inspect some of the building stones which have appeared more recently. The excursion commences in Mosley Street adjacent to St. Peter's Square and finishes in Market Street adjacent to the Arndale Centre, near Piccadilly. Locality numbers in the text relate to those on the street map (Figure 20). Because premises change hands frequently these days, addresses as well as current occupiers of buildings are given. This excursion can be done in greater safety on Sundays when traffic is light; on the other hand, access to interior concourses is normally only possible in working hours. Possession of the set of Building Stones Postcards available from the Extra Mural Department of Manchester University, museum shops, etc., would be an advantage.

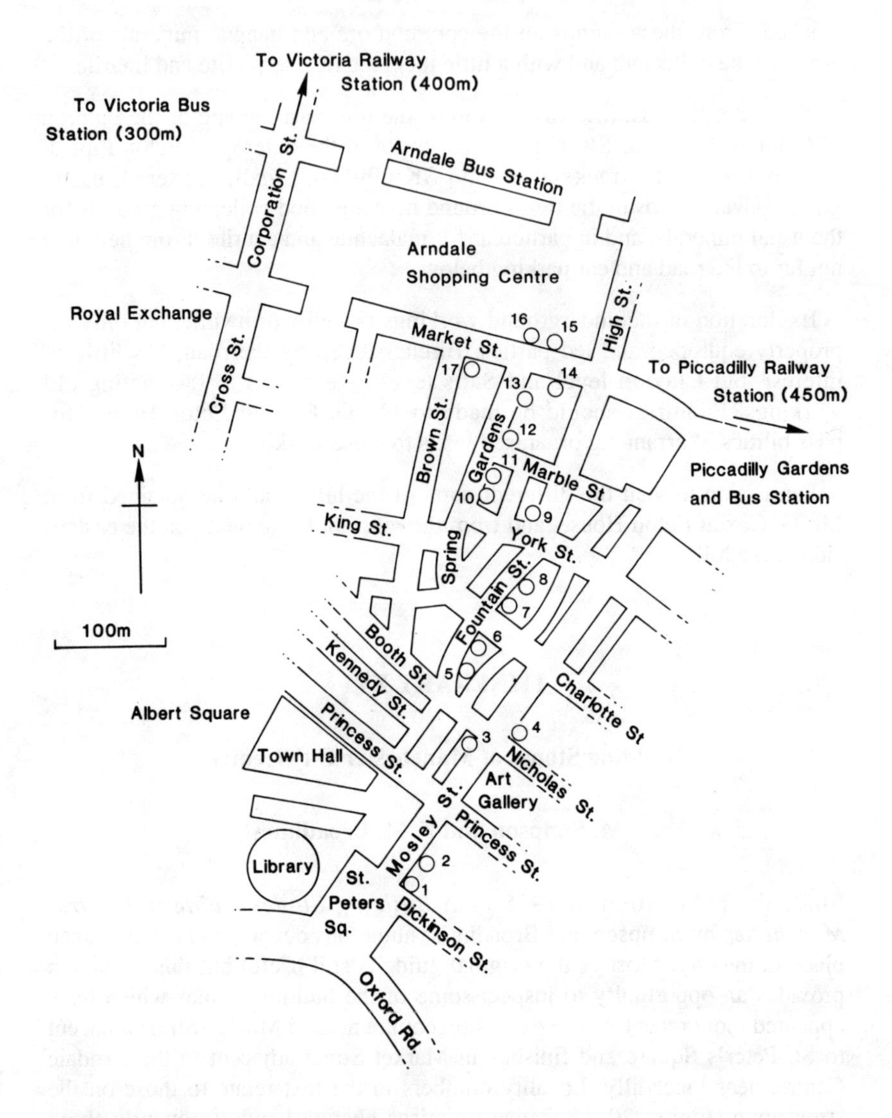

Figure 20. Map of central Manchester.

Route. Locality 1. On the south side of Mosley Street at its junction with St. Peter's Square and Dickinson Street the corner building, Century House (90, Dickinson Street), currently occupied by the Bank of Credit and Commerce International, is not a new building but has been cleaned. The result is disappointing but at least the stone in the building can be readily identified as *Portland Stone* with conspicuous bivalve fossils set in an oolitic matrix. Although buff-coloured when fresh, Portland Stone generally becomes white on weathering and this example is no exception. At ground level *South West England Granite* has been used.

Locality 2. At 87-89, Mosley Street there is a magnificent display of *Balmoral Red Granite* from Finland, but with a Scottish-sounding name acquired at one of its main entry points to the U.K., Aberdeen. The granite is seen not only on the outside of the building but also in the sheltered entrance area so can be inspected in comfort regardless of the weather. Note the pink feldspar, translucent quartz and black ferro-magnesian minerals.

Cross Princess Street and in the continuation of Mosley Street, opposite to the City Art Gallery (with its exterior of Carboniferous sandstones, see Simpson & Broadhurst, 1975, for details), stop at No. 74, Mosley Street.

Locality 3. No. 74, Mosley Street, Abbey House, currently a branch of the Abbey National Building Society. The most striking feature here is the use of *Carboniferous Sandstone* in combination with *Rapakivi Granite* (also known as *Baltic Brown*) at pavement level. At the entrance to the building the granite has been used in the floor, and here, is largely unpolished to provide a non-slip surface. Strips of polished granite provides a pleasing contrast to the unpolished areas. The spherical pink feldspars (circular in section) characteristic of this granite are well seen here. Inclusion of other minerals, seen as concentric bands, indicate that feldspar formation was not continuous but spasmodic. This granite is quarried in Finland, close to the USSR border at Kotka. Inside the building the internal walls are lined by *travertine*, a banded rock formed by precipitation of calcium carbonate by hot (volcanic) springs emerging after passage through underground limestone formations. Travertine is forming today in parts of Yellowstone National Park, for instance. The travertine in Abbey House came from the formerly volcanic district of Tivoli to the east of Rome. Travertine always contains many cavities which are generally filled with cement when used, as here, as decorative stone. On the floor inside the building are tiles made up of pieces of limestone bound by a resin-bound matrix. This material takes a good polish.

Locality 4. Obliquely opposite to Abbey House on Mosley Street is No. 75, currently occupied by a branch of the Bristol and West Building Society. This building is faced by panels of *Portland Roach*, a limestone in which the shells of numerous fossil bivalves and gastropods have been dissolved to reveal both external and internal moulds. Excellent panels with fossils are to be seen on Nicholas Street. This building was described by Simpson & Broadhurst, 1975. Walk down Booth Street to Fountain Street and turn right.

Locality 5. 81, Fountain Street, Wigoder House. This building has a stone facade of a pink-and-grey gneiss with spectacular banding. Note that the banding arises from segregations of minerals, the pink bands consisting dominantly of feldspars, the grey of ferromagnesian minerals. This gneiss, known as *Multicolour* comes from the neighbourhood of Kanakapura, south of Bangalore, Kornataka State, southern India. Around the doorway is an area of highly polished limestone panels. Such panels are generally referred to by the building trade, incorrectly, as "marbles". This particular example is know as *Botticino 'Marble'*. It comes from Brescia, Lombardy, Italy. The characteristic irregular, brown, lines are stylolites, composed of insoluble materials left after partial solution of the limestone when it came under pressure (e.g. by the weight of overlying rock formations or by tectonic pressure). From Wigoder House continue, eastwards, to No. 77, Fountain Street.

Locality 6. 77, Fountain Street, Brook House. The exterior of this building is graced with *South West England Granite*.

Locality 7. Junction of Fountain Street and Spring Gardens, 55, Spring Gardens, Brook Street Industrial. This building is faced by two rock types. One, at pavement level, is almost totally black and is known as *Ebony Black*. The other at higher levels, is dark grey and known as *Bon Accord*. The Ebony Black is also used in the floor at one of the entrances to the building and here strips of polished material alternate with strips of unpolished stone. Both rocks are gabbros, the dark hues resulting from a high proportion of iron and magnesium minerals in the rock. Material of this type is available from more than one source but the most likely is the Johannesburg area of South Africa. Continue eastwards.

Locality 8. 53, Fountain Street, Barnet House. This building is adorned by panels of *Carrara Marble*, a white stone crossed by irregular grey stripes. Unfortunately, a covering of anti-graffiti paint obscures much detail of this rock and discussion about marble is left until later. Continue eastwards as far as York Street.

Locality 9. Junction of Fountain Street and York Street. Two buildings here have been described by Simpson & Broadhurst, 1975. At 40, Fountain Street, the Barclays Bank exhibits a granodiorite *(Silver White)* from near Trondheim in Norway and another *Ebony Black* gabbro, but this time from Sweden. Also 40, Fountain Street, the Oddfellows House shows *Lakeland Green Slate* from the Ordovician of the Lake District. Opposite Oddfellows House the building at 44, York Street has walls of brick and reconstituted stone but with a remarkable band at pavement level of gneiss with pink feldspar-rich bands alternating with light grey bands richer in ferromagnesian minerals. In places the bands are tightly folded and many minerals or mineral aggregates aligned parallel to the axial plane of the folds. The rock comes from Westervik, southern Sweden, and despite being a gneiss is known as *Arcus Granite*. Continue, northwards, along York Street.

Locality 10. 3, York Street. A magnificent building of red sandstone, with a grey granite (carrying dark grey xenoliths) displayed at pavement level. The inside of this building, currently accessible via Greens Cafe Bar is adorned with spectacular displays of polished breccias (fractured rock comprising angular fragments). The fragments (green) are composed of serpentinite, a much altered ultrabasic rock thought to be derived from the uppermost part of the Earth's mantle and emplaced into the overlying crust as thrust slices within a compression belt. The fragments are enclosed by calcite. Marbles high on the wall are probably from Carrara (white, grey stripes) and Sienna (brown). From York Street turn eastwards into Spring Gardens.

Locality 11. Tootal House. The exterior of this building is clad with *Rapakivi (Baltic Brown) Granite*, similar to that already seen in Mosley Street. The interior concourse walls are covered with a brown filled, travertine. Continue eastwards, along Spring Gardens to the junction with Marble Street.

Locality 12. 17, Marble Street, Lowry House. Despite its address the exterior surfaces of this building are made of concrete which largely explains why its appearance is so dull. However, there is ample compensation in that the interior concourse is lined by an attractive marble which, unlike the Carrara varieties, is adorned with brown bands and pink patches. In true marbles, like this example, heating under pressure has caused the calcite, in what was originally a limestone, to recrystallise in the form of equal-sized calcite grains. This feature is well seen here. Light reflected from cleavage faces within the calcite crystals produces a sparkling effect and is most attractive. This marble comes from Portugal under the name of *Pale Aurora*. Continue along Spring Gardens.

Locality 13. 11, Spring Gardens. National Westminster Bank. There is more concrete here but its appearance is marginally improved by the inclusion of an aggregate made up of chippings derived from the crushing of a granite, a granite which could well have been the Shap Granite of Cumbria. Much more attractive than the concrete are extensive surfaces of *Rapakavi (Baltic Brown) Granite*. Bands of fine-grained granitic (aplite) material are to be seen cutting through rock. Some of these veins are associated with patches of particularly coarse-grained (pegmatitic) material. Inclusions (xenoliths) of fine-grained granite are also to be seen. Inside the building travertine has been used in both floors and walls. Continue eastwards to the junction of Spring Gardens with the pedestrianised Market Street. Here turn right (southwards).

Locality14. 88, Market Street. McDonald's Golden Arches Restaurant. The exterior surfaces of these premises are formed of a spectacular travertine, the variety *St. John* from Italy. This travertine has been filled. Examine the detail of bedding carefully. In places there is evidence of much disruption of the bedding. This is because the hot springs, responsible for the supply of calcium carbonate, frequently change location so that deposits already laid down are broken up and reincorporated into later deposits. Cross over Market Street to No. 57.

Locality 15. 57, Market Street. British Home Stores. On the outside of this building, adjacent to the entrances, there are small areas of granite panelling to be seen. However, the granite is superbly displayed over a large area on the walls of the concourse just inside the entrance. The granite has an overall pleasing red-brown colour. On close inspection the component grains (minerals) include quartz which, instead of appearing translucent or grey, as in most granites, is here a light blue colour and makes this particular granite easy to identify. The granite is known as *Imperial Mahogany* and is quarried from the Precambrian of the Black Hills in South Dakota, U.S.A. Seen from a distance the rock frequently displays a banded structure, the bands being formed by segregation of particular minerals. The rock is therefore really transitional between a granite and a gneiss. From British Home Stores proceed to the next store (to the North).

Locality 16. Unit 2, Arndale Centre. Market Street. Littlewoods. The external surfaces of *Rapakivi (Baltic Brown) Granite* should present no problem. The round pink feldspars (orthoclase) are rimmed by a green feldspar (plagioclase), a feature of Rapakivi well seen here. Note the presence of fine-grained granite inclusions (xenoliths). Cross Market Street, but continue to the North.

Locality 17. 66, Market Street. Dolcis. The shop frontage consists of grey-striped *Carrara Marble*. This stone dominantly composed of calcite, like all other marbles and limestones, is susceptible to weathering, especially by acid rain. It is not normally recommended for external use in cities such as Manchester where the atmosphere is polluted. It will be of interest to see how this Carrara Marble fares. Note that the marble in the floor at the entrance has been reinforced by strips of artificial stone to guard against the wear caused by shoes. Calcite is a soft mineral.

REFERENCES

ADAM, W., 1848. *Gem of the Peak.* 4th Edition, Derby.

AITKENHEAD, N. and CHISHOLM, J. I. 1982. A standard nomenclature for the Dinantian formations of the Peak District of Derbyshire and Staffordshire. Report 82/8. *Institute of Geological Sciences.*

AITKENHEAD, N., CHISHOLM, J. N. and STEPHENSON, I. P., 1985. Geology of the country around Buxton, Leek and Bakewell. *Mem. Brit. Geol. Surv.,* H.M. Stationery Office, 168 pp.

ALTY, S. W., 1926. The Petrographic Features of Keuper Rocks from a Boring at Wilmslow near Stockport, Cheshire. *Proc. Lpool. geol., Soc.* **14,** 278-83.

ANDERTON, R., BRIDGES, P. H., LEEDER, M. R. and SELLWOOD, B. W., 1979. *A dynamic stratigraphy of the British Isles.* George Allen and Unwin.

ARNOLD-BEMROSE, H. H., 1907. The toadstones of Derbyshire, their field relations and petrography. *Q. Jl. Geol. Soc. Lond.,* **63,** 241-281.

ARTHURTON, R. S., 1980. Rhythmic sedimentary sequences in the Triassic Keuper Marl (Mercia Mudstone Group) of Cheshire, northwest England. *Geol. Journ.* **15,** 43-58.

BAKEWELL, R., 1811. Account of a Cobalt Mine in *Cheshire Monthly Magazine,* **31,** 7-9.

BAKEWELL, R., 1813. *An introduction to Geology.* London. (See Appendix re The Cobalt Mine).

BATESON, J. H., 1982. Geochemical reconnaisance in the Cheshire Basin. A report prepared for the Department of Industry. *Mineral Reconnaisance Programme Report No. 52,* London, HMSO for IGS, 12 pp.

BATHURST, R. G. C., HARPER, J. C., EAGAR, R. M. C., NEAVERSON, E., BANNERJEE, A., BRENCHLEY, P. J., OLDERSHAWE, A. E., SHANLIN, J. K. and STARKEY, J., 1965. *Geology around University Towns: Liverpool.* Geologists' Association Guide No. 6, 40 pp.

BELL, H. S., 1940. Armoured Mudballs – Their Origin, Properties and Role in Sedimentation. *J. Geol.,* 14 1-31.

BOULTON, G. S., 1972. Modern Arctic glaciers as depositional models for former ice sheets. *Jl. geol. Soc. Lond.* **128,** 361-394.

BRAITHWAITE, R. S. W., 1983. Minerals of the Derbyshire orefield. *The Mineralogical Record*, **14,** 15-24.

BRAITHWAITE, R. S. W., GREENLAND, T. B. and RYBACK, G., 1963. Celestine and aurichalcite from Clayton adit, Ecton Hill, Wetton, Staffordshire. Exhibit. *Mineralogical Magazine*, **33,** lxxxvi.

BRAITHWAITE, R. S. W. and KNIGHT, J. R., 1968. Serpierite from Ecton, Staffordshire. *Mineralogical Magazine,* **36,** 882.

BRAITHWAITE, R. S. W., RYBACK, G. and GREENLAND, T. B., 1963. Stalactitic hydrozincite from Ecton mines, Wetton, Staffordshire. Exhibit. *Mineralogical Magazine,* **33,** lxxxvi.

BRISTOW, C. S., 1988. Controls on the sedimentation of the Rough Rock Group (Namurian) from the Pennine Basin of northern England. In (Besly, B. M. and Kelling, G; Editors). *Sedimentation in a synorogenic complex.* Blackie.

BROADHURST, F. M. 1959. Day excursion to an area south of Glossop. In (Eagar R.M.C. *et al*). *The Area around Manchester* (1st ed.) Geologists' Association Guide No. 7.

BROADHURST, F. M., 1982. Geology in Vernon and Woodbank Parks, Stockport. *Amateur Geologist,* X, (2), 11-15.

BROADHURST, F. M., EAGAR, R. M. C., JACKSON, J. W., SIMPSON, I. M. and THOMPSON, D. B., 1970. *The Area around Manchester*. Geologists' Association Guide No. 7, 51 pp.

BROADHURST, F. M. and FRANCE, A. A., 1986. Time represented by coal seams in the Coal Measures of England. *Internat. Journ. Coal. Geol.*, **6,** 43-54.

BROMEHEAD, C. E. N., EDWARDS, W., WRAY, D. A. and STEPHENS, J. V., 1933. The Geology of the country around Holmfirth and Glossop. *Mem. Geol. Surv. Engl. & Wales.*

BROOKFIELD, M. E., 1977. The origin of bounding surfaces in ancient aeolian sandstones. *Sedimentology*, **24,** 303-332.

BROOKFIELD, M. E., 1984. Eolian Sands. In (Walker, R. G; Ed) *Facies Models* 2nd Edition. Hamilton (Ontario), Geoscience Canada, 91-103.

CALVER, M. A., 1969. Westphalian of Britain. *Comptes Rendus 6' me Internal Congr. Strat. Géol. Carbonifère* (Sheffield, 1966), **1,** 233-254.

CARLON, C. J., 1975. The Geology and Geochemistry of some British barite deposits. Unpublished Ph. D. Thesis, University of Manchester, 335 pp.

CARLON, C. J., 1979. *The Alderley Edge Mines, Altrincham*. J. Sherratt & Sons, 144 pp.

CARLON, C., 1981. The Gallantry Bank Copper Mine, Bickerton, Cheshire. *British Mining* No. 16, Sheffield, Northern Mine Research Society, 50 pp.

CARLON, C. J. and THOMPSON, D. B., 1981. Aspects of mineralisation within the Cheshire Basin. (Abstract). *Jl. geol. Soc. Lond.* **138**, p220. (See Conference Report by Iveson, J. R., 1981. Low-Temperature mineralisation. *Jl. geol. Soc. Lond.* **138,** 217-220.

CHISHOLM, J. I., 1990. The Upper Band – Better Bed sequence (Lower Coal Measures, Westphalian A) in the central and south Pennine area of England. *Geol. Mag.*, **127,** 55-74.

CLEGG, J. A., ALMOND, M. and STUBBS, P. H., 1954. The Remanent Magnetism of some Sedimentary Rocks in Britain. *Phil. Mag,* **45,** 583-98.

COLLINSON, J. D., 1976. Deltaic evolution during basin fill. Namurian of the central Pennines, England (Abstr.). *Amer. Assoc. Petrol. Geol. Bull.*, **60,** 52.

COLLINSON, J. D., 1988. Controls on Namurian sedimentation in the Central Province basins of northern England. In (Besley, B. M. and Kelling, G; Eds). *Sedimentology in a synorogenic basin complex*: the *Upper Carboniferous of NW Europe*, 85-101. Blackie.

COLTER, V. S. and BARR, K. W., 1975. Recent developments in the geology of the Irish Sea and Cheshire Basins. In (Woodland, A; Ed). *Petroleum and the continental Shelf of Northwest Europe*. Vol 1, Geology, London, Applied Science Pub., 61-75.

COPE, F. W., 1949. Correlation of the Coal Measures of Macclesfield and the Goyt Trough. *Trans. Instn. Min. Engrs.*, **108,** 1-18.

COPE, F. W., 1965. *The Peak District, Derbyshire*. Geologists' Association Guide No. 26, 26 pp.

CRITCHLEY, M. F., 1979. A geological outline of the Ecton copper mines, Staffordshire. *Bulletin of the Peak District Mines Historical Society*, **7,** 4, 177-191.

DAVIDSON, C. F., 1965. A possible mode of origin of stratabound copper ores. *Econ. Geol.*, **60,** 942-954.

DAVIDSON, C. F., 1966. Some genetic relationships between ore deposits and evaporites. *Trans. Inst. Mining. Metall.*, **75,** B216-225.

DEWEY, H. and EASTWOOD, T., 1925. Copper ores of the Midlands, Wales and the Lake District and the Isle of *Man. Geol. Surv. Grt. Brit. Min. Res. Mem.* 30. 87 pp.

EAGAR, R. M. C., 1947. A study of a non-marine lamellibranch succession in the *Anthraconaia lenisulcata* Zone of the Yorkshire Coal Measures. *Phil. Trans Roy. Soc. Lond.*, **B233,** 1-54.

EAGAR, R. M. C., 1951. A revision of the sequence and correlation of the Lower Coal Measures west of Wigan. *Quart. Journ. Geol. Soc. Lond.*, **107,** 23-50.

EAGAR, R. M. C., 1952. The succession above the Soft Bed and Bassy Mine in the Pennine region. *Lpool & Manchr. Geol. Journ.*, **1,** 23-56.

EAGAR, R. M. C., 1956. Additions to the non-marine fauna of the Lower Coal Measures of the north-midlands coalfields. *Lpool & Manchr. Geol. Journ.*, **1,** 328-369.

EAGAR, R. M. C., 1985. The Geological Column, a Manchester Museum publication. Sixth (revised) Edition. Printguide, Southmoor Road, Wythenshawe, Manchester M23 9NR.

EAGAR, R. M. C., BAINES, J. G., COLLINSON, J. D., HARDY, P. G., OKOLO, S. A. and POLLARD, J. E., 1985. Trace fossil assemblages and their occurence in Silesian (mid-Carboniferous) deltaic sediments of the Central Pennine Basin, England. In (A. A. Curran; Ed). *Biogenic Structures: Their Use in Interpreting Depositional Systems.* Soc. Econ. Paleont & Mineralog. Spec. Publ. No. 35.

EARP, J. R., MAGRAW, D., POOLE, E. G., LAND, D. H. and WHITEMAN, A. J., 1961. Geology of the country around Clitheroe and Nelson. *Mem. Geol. Surv. G.B.*

EVANS, W. B., WILSON, A. A., TAYLOR, B. J. and PRICE, D., 1968. Geology of the country around Macclesfield, Congleton, Crewe and Middlewich. *Mem. Geol. Surv. G.B.*

FAREY, J., 1811. *A general view of the agriculture and minerals of Derbyshire.* Vol. **1.** MacMillan.

FITCH, F. J., MILLER, J. A. and THOMPSON, D. B., 1966. The palaeogeographic significance of isotopic age determinations on detrital micas from the Triassic of the Stockport-Macclesfield district, Cheshire. *Palaeogeogr. Palaeoclimatol. Palaeoecol* **2,** 281-313.

FORD, T. D., 1969 The Stratiform Ore-deposits of Derbyshire. pp. 73-96. In (James, J. H; ed). *Sedimentary Ores: ancient and modern* (revised). Leicester, Department of Geology.

FORD, T. D. and KING, R. J., 1968. Mineralisation in the Triassic rocks of South Derbyshire, *Trans. Inst. Min. Metall.*, **77,** 42-47.

FORD T. D. and SERJEANT, W. A. S., 1964. The Peak District Mineral Index. *Bulletin of the Peak District Mines Historical Society*, **2,** 122-150.

FRIEND, P. F., 1966. Clay fractions and colours of some Devonian red beds in the Catskill Mountains, USA. *Quart, Jl. geol. Soc. Lond.*, **122,** 273-292.

GALE, I. N., EVANS, C. J., EVANS, R. B., SMITH, I. F., HOUGHTON, M. T. and BURGESS, W. G., 1984. The Permo-Triassic aquifers of the Cheshire and West Lancashire Basins, Investigations of the geothermal potential of the U.K. British Geological Survey, Keyworth. 49 pp.

GARNER, R., 1844. T*he natural history of the county of Staffordshire*. London.

GAWTHORPE, R. L., 1987. Tectonic-sedimentary evolution of the Bowland Basin, northern England, during the Dinantian. *Journ, Geol. Soc. Lond.*, **144,** 59-72.

GAWTHORPE, R. L., GUTTERIDGE, P. and LEEDER, M. R., 1989. Late Devonian and Dinantian basin evolution in northern England and north Wales. In (Arthurton, R. S., Gutteridge, P. and Nolan, S. C; eds). *The Role of Tectonics in Devonian and Carboniferous Sedimentation in the British Isles*. Occas. Publ. No. 6, Yorks. Geol. Soc., 1-23.

GRAYSON, R. F., 1981. *Salthill Quarry geology trail*. Geology and Physiography Section, Nature Conservancy Council.

GREEN, A. H. and STRAHAN, A., 1887. Geology of the Carboniferous Limestone, Yoredale Rocks and Millstone Grit of North Derbyshire. *Memoirs of the Geological Survey of England and Wales*. 2nd Edition.

GREENWELL, G. C., 1866. On the Copper Sandstone of Alderley Edge, Cheshire. *Proc. S. Wales Inst. Eng.*, **4,** 44-9.

GREENWOOD, H. W., 1919. The Trias of the Macclesfield district. *Proc. Liverpool Geol. Soc.*, **12,** 325-337.

GREENWOOD, H. W., 1920 (1918). On the distribution and significance of barium compounds in sedimentary rocks with special reference to the Trias. *Proc. Liverpool Geol. Soc.,* **12,** 355-361.

GREENWOOD, H. W., 1921. On certain mineral deposits in stratified rocks with special reference to the Carboniferous and the Trias. *Proc. Lpool. Geol. Soc.,* **13,** 122-136.

HARDY, P. G., 1970. Aspects of palaeoecology in arenaceous sediments of Upper Carboniferous age in the area around Manchester. Ph. D. Thesis, University of Manchester, U.K.

HOWELL, F. T., 1973. The subdrift surface of the Mersey and Weaver catchment and adjacent areas. *Geol. Journ.*, **8,** 285-296.

HOLMES, I., CHAMBERS, A. D., IXER, R. A., TURNER, P. and VAUGHAN, D. J., 1983. Diagenetic Processes and the Mineralisation in the Triassic of Central England. *Mineral. Deposita,* **18,** 365-377.

HULL, E., 1864. On the copper-bearing rocks of Alderley Edge. *Geol. Mag.*, **1,** 65-9.

HUNTER, R. E., 1977. Basic types of stratification in small aeolian dunes. *Sedimentology*, **24,** 361-387.

IRELAND, R. J., POLLARD, J. E., STEEL, R. J. and THOMPSON, D.B., 1978. Intertidal sediments and trace fossils from the Waterstones (Scythian - Anisian?) at Daresbury, Cheshire. *Proc. Yorks. geol. Soc.*, **41,** 399-435.

IXER, R. A., 1978. The distribution of bravoite and nickelferous marcasite in central Britain. *Min, Mag.*, **42,** 149-50.

IXER, R. and VAUGHAN, D. J., 1982. The primary ore mineralogy of the Alderley Edge deposit, Cheshire. *Min. Mag.*, **46,** 485-492.

JARZEMBOWSKI, E. A., 1989. A century plus of fossil insects. *Proc. Geol. Ass.,* **100,** 433-449.

JOHNSON, R. H., 1965. A study of the Charlesworth landslides near Glossop, North Derbyshire. *Trans. Inst. Br. Geogr.*, **37,** 111-125.

JOHNSON, R. H., 1969. The glacial geomorphology of the area around Hyde, Cheshire. *Proc. Yorks. geol. Soc.*, **37,** 189-230.

JOHNSON, R. H., 1969. A Reconnaissance survey of some river terraces in part of the Mersey and Weaver catchment. *Mem. Proc. Manchr. Lit. Phil. Soc.*, **112,** 1-35.

JOHNSON, R. H., 1985. The imprint of glaciation on the West Pennine Uplands. In (R. H. Johnson; Ed). *The Geomorphology of North West England* (Manchester U. P.) 237-62.

JOHNSON, R. H., 1989. The Late Glacial and Post Glacial History of the River Goyt: Some Further Evidence. *The Manchester Geographer*, **10,** 26-41.

JOHNSON, N. C., 1984. Brynlow Mine, Alderley Edge – An Eighteenth Century Working. *The Journal of the Derbyshire Caving Club*, 8-13.

JOHNSON, N. C., 1984. Wizard's Well Mine, Alderley Edge — Early Nineteenth Century Cobalt Workings. *The Journal of the Derbyshire Caving Club,* 17-21.

JONES, O. T., 1924. The Origin of the Manchester Plain. *J. Manchester Geogr. Soc.*, 39-40, 89-124.

KING, R. J., 1966. Episyngenetic mineralisation in the English Midlands. *Mercian Geol.*, **1,** 291-302.

KING, R. J. and FORD, T. D., 1968. Mineralisation. In (Sylvester-Bradley, P.C. and Ford, T. D; eds). *Geology of the East Midlands*. Leicester, Leicester Univ. Press. Chapter 7.

KINGSBURY, A. W. G., 1956. A note on the origin of Mottramite from Mottram St Andrew *in* Kingsbury, A. W. G. & Hartley, J. New occurrences of vanadium minerals (mottramite, descloizite and vanadinite in the Caldbeck area of Cumberland. *Min. Mag.*, **31,** 289-95.

KIRKHAM, N., 1961. Ecton Mines. *Peak District Mines Historical Society Special Publication* No. 1.

KLEIN, G. de V., 1962. Sedimentary structures in the Keuper Marl. *Geol. Mag.*, **99,** 137-144.

LEEDER, M. R., 1988. Recent developments in Carboniferous Geology: a critical review with implications for the British Isles and N. W. Europe. *Proc. Geol. Ass.*, **99,** 78-100.

LOVELL, J. P. B., 1977. *The British Isles through Geological Time. A northward drift*. London, Allen and Unwin, 40 pp.

MANNING, D. A. C., 1990. The copper mineralisation of Alderley Edge. New views on a well known viewpoint. *Amateur Geologist*, **13,** 50-52.

McKEE, E. D., 1966. Dune Structures. *Sedimentology*, **7,** 1-69.

MAWE, J., 1802. *The mineralogy of Derbyshire with a description of the most interesting mines in the north of England.* Phillips, London.

MILLER, G. D., 1988. The Carlton Hill S. S. I. – and update. *Amateur Geologist* **12/2,** 31-39.

MILLER, J. and GRAYSON, R. F., 1972. New evidence on the origin and structure of the Lower Visean 'reef' limestones near Clitheroe, Lancs. *Proc. Yorks. Geol. Soc.*, **38,** 667-635.

MITCHELL, J. G. and TAKA, A. S., 1984. Potassium and argon loss patterns in weathered micas: implications for detrital mineral studies, with particular reference to the Triassic palaeogeography of the British Isles. *Sediment. Geol*, **39,** 27-52.

MOHR, P. A., 1964. On the copper-mineralised sandstones of Alderley Edge, England and Chercher, Ethiopia, and the problem of their genesis; an essay on Red Bed Copper deposits. *Contrib. Geophys. Observatory Fac. Sci. Haile Selassie Univ, Addis Ababa*, Series A Vol 4.

NAYLOR, H., TURNER, P., VAUGHAN, D. J., BOYCE, A. J., and FALLICK, A. E., 1989. Genetic studies of red bed mineralisation in the Triassic of the Cheshire Basin, northwest England. *Journ. geol. Soc. Land.*, **146,** 685-699.

PITTY, A. F., 1965. A study of some escarpment gaps in the southern Pennines. *Trans. Inst. Br. Geogr.*, **37,** 127-146.

POLLARD, J. E., 1981. A comparison between the Triassic trace fossils of Cheshire and South Germany. *Palaeontology*, **24,** 555-558.

PORTER, L., 1969. Ecton Hill – a study of the surface features. *Bulletin of the Peak District Mines Historical Society*, **4,** 159-169.

PORTER, L., 1970. Ecton Hill, Part II – underground. *Bulletin of the Peak District Mines Historical Society*, **4,** 195-216.

PRESS, F. and SIEVER, R., 1982. *Earth.* 3rd Revised Edition. W. H. Freeman and Co., San Francisco.

RAMSBOTTOM, W. H. C., 1981. Eustacy, sea level and local tectonism, with examples from the British Carboniferous. *Proc. Yorks, Geol. Soc.* **43,** 473-482.

RAMSBOTTOM, W. H. C., CALVER, M. A., EAGER, R. M. C., HODSON, F., HALLIDAY, D. W., STUBBLEFIELD, C. J. and WILSON, R. B., 1978. *A correlation of Silesian rocks in the British Isles*. Geol. Soc. Lond. Spec. Rept., No. 10.

RICE, R. J., 1957. Some aspects of the glacial and post-glacial history of the Lower Goyt valley, Cheshire. *Proc. Geol. Assoc.*, **68,** 217-27.

ROBEY, J. A. and PORTER, L., 1972. *The copper and lead mines of Ecton Hill, Staffordshire*. Moorland Publishing Co., and Peak District Mines Historical Society.

ROBINSON, P. L., 1973. Palaeoclimatology and continental drift. In (Tarling, D. H. & Runcorn, S. K; eds). *Implications of Continental Drift to the Earth Sciences*, Vol. 1, London, Academic Press, 449-474.

ROEDER, C., 1901. Prehistoric and Subsequent Mining at Alderley Edge with a Sketch of the Archaeological Features of the Neighbourhood. *Trans. Lancs. Chesh. Antiq. Soc.*, **19,** 77-116.

ROSCOE, Sir H. E., 1868. Researches on Vanadium. *Phil. Trans. roy. Soc.*, **158,** 4-6.

ROSCOE, Sir H. E., 1869. Researches on Vanadium. *Phil. Trans. roy. Soc.*, **158,** 1-27.

ROSCOE, Sir H. E., 1876. On two new vanadium minerals. *Proc. roy. Soc.*, **25,** 109-112.

ROSE, MARY B., 1986. *The Gregs of Quarry Bank Mill. The rise and decline of a family firm*, 1750-1914.

RUSSEL, Sir A., 1919. (On the nature, potential and origin of the mineral deposits at Alderley Edge). Unpublished, untitled Report. (Copy available from the keeper of Geology. University of Manchester Museum, Oxford Road, Manchester).

SANDIFORD, A. W. and ASHFORTH, T. E., 1983. *The Forgotten Valley*. Bury and District Local History Society.

SCHOFIELD, K. and ADAMS, A. E., 1985. Stratigraphy and depositional environments of the Woo Dale Limestones Formation (Dinantian) Derbyshire. *Proc. Yorks. geol. Soc.*, **45,** 225-233.

SCHOFIELD, K. and ADAMS, A. E., 1986. Burial delomitization of the Woo Dale Limestones Formation (Lower Carboniferous), Derbyshire, England. *Sedimentology*, **33,** 207-219.

SERJEANT, W. A. S., 1956a. The mineralogy of Ecton Hill. *Journal of the University of Sheffield Geological Society*, **2,** 87-92.

SERJEANT, W. A. S., 1956b. Some Derbyshire mineral localities. *Journal of the University of Sheffield Geological Society*, **2,** 114-121.

SERJEANT, W. A. S., 1957. Further Derbyshire mineral localities. *Journal of the University of Sheffield Geological Society*, **2,** 172-179.

SIBSON, R. H., McMOORE, J. and RANKIN, J. H., 1975. Seismic pumping – a hydrothermal fluid transport mechanism. *Jl. geol. Soc. Lond*, **131,** 635-659.

SIMPSON, I. M., 1959. The Pleistocene succession in the Stockport South Manchester area. *J. Geol. Soc. Lond.*, **115,** 107-19.

SIMPSON, I. M. and BROADHURST, F. M., 1975. *A Building Stones Guide to Central Manchester*. Department of Extra Mural Studies, University of Manchester.

SMITH, W. (Ed), 1953. *A Scientific Survey of Merseyside*. Liverpool, Brit. Ass. Adv. Sci. Regional Handbook.

STEVENSON, I. P. and GAUNT, G. D., 1971. Geology of the country around Chapel-en-le-Frith. *Mem. geol. Surv. GB*. 444 pp.

STARKEY, R. E., 1983. On the occurrence of millerite at Ecton Hill, Staffordshire. *Journal of the Russell Society*, **1,** 16-18.

TAYLOR, B. J., PRICE, R. H. and TROTTER, F. M., 1963. The Geology of the country around Stockport and Knutsford. *Mem. Geol. Surv. G.B.*, 183 pp.

THOMPSON, D. B., 1966a. The occurence of an Insect Wing and Branchiopods (Euestheria) in the Lower Këuper Marl at Styal, Cheshire. *Mercian Geologist*, **1,** 237-245.

THOMPSON, D. B., 1966b. Some Aspects of the Stratigraphy and Sedimentology of the NE of the Permo-Triassic Cheshire Basin, with Special Reference to the Lower Keuper Sandstones Formation. Unpublished M. Sc. thesis, Manchester University 359 pp.

THOMPSON, D. B., 1966c. Some aspects of mineralisation at Alderley Edge. Unpublished MS.

THOMPSON, D. B., 1969. Dome-shaped aeolian dunes in the Frodsham Member of the so-called "Keuper" Sandstone Formation (Scythian-?Anisian:Triassic) at Frodsham, Cheshire (England). *Sediment. Geol.*, **3,** 263-289.

THOMPSON, D. B., 1970a. The stratigraphy of the so-called Keuper Sandstone Formation (Scythian-?Anisian) in the Permo-Triassic Cheshire Basin. *Q.Jl. geol. Soc. Lond.*, **126,** 151-181.

THOMPSON, D. B., 1970b. Sedimentation of the Triassic (Scythian) Red Pebbly Sandstones in the Cheshire Basin and its margins. *Geol. J.*, **7,** 183-216.

THOMPSON, D. B., 1985. *Field Excursion to the Permo-Triassic of the Cheshire and Adjacent Basins* (4th Edit). Chester, Poroperm-Geochem, 172 pp.

THOMPSON, D. B. and WORSLEY, P., 1967. Periods of Ventifact Formation in the Permo-Triassic and Quaternary of East Cheshire. *Mercian Geologist*, **2,** 279-298.

TONKS, L. H., JONES, R. C. B., LLOYD, W. and SHERLOCK, R. L., 1931. The Geology of Manchester and the South-East Lancashire Coalfield. *Mem. Geol. Surv. Engl. and Wales.*

WARRINGTON, G., 1963. The Occurrence of the Branchiopod Crustacean *Euestheria* in the Keuper Sandstone of Alderley Edge, Cheshire. *Lpool. Manchr. geol. J.*, **3,** 315-19.

WARRINGTON, G., 1965. The Metalliferous Mining District of Alderley Edge, Cheshire. *Mercian Geologist,* **1,** 111-131.

WARRINGTON, G., 1967. Correlation of the Keuper Series of the Triassic by Miospores. *Nature, Lond.*, **214,** 1323-4.

WARRINGTON, G., 1980. The Alderley Edge Mining District. *Amateur Geologist,* **8,** 4-13.

WARRINGTON, G., 1981. The Copper Mines of Alderley Edge and Mottram St. Andrew, Cheshire. *Journal of the Chester Archaeological Society*, **64,** 47-73.

WARRINGTON, G., AUDLEY-CHARLES, M. G., ELLIOTT, R. E., EVANS, W. B., IVIMEY-COOK, H. C., KENT, P. E., ROBINSON, P. L., SHOTTON, F. W., and TAYLOR, F. M.,1980. *A correlation of Triassic rocks in the British Isles,* Spec. Rep. geol. Soc. London, **13,** 78 pp.

WARRINGTON, G., and THOMPSON, D. B.,1971. The Triassic Rocks of Alderley Edge, Cheshire. *Mercian Geologist*, **4,** 69-72.

WHITTAKER, A. (Ed.), 1985. *Atlas of Onshore Sedimentary Basins in England and Wales.* (Memoir and case maps). Edinburgh, Blackie for the British Geological Survey.

WIGNALL, P. B., 1987. A biofacies analysis of the Gastrioceras cumbriense Marine Band (Namurian) of the Central Pennines. *Yorks. geol. Soc.* **46,** 111-121.

WRIGHT, W. B., SHERLOCK, R. L., WRAY, D. A., LLOYD, W. and TONKS, L. H., 1927. The Geology of the Rossendale Anticline. *Mem. Geol. Surv. Engl. and Wales.*

WRIGHT, D. A., SHERLOCK, R. L., WRAY, D. A., LLOYD, W. and TONKS, L. H., 1927. The geology of the Rossendale Anticline. *Mem. Geol. Surv. Engl. and Wales.*

ZIEGLER, P. A., 1981. Evolution of Sedimentary Basins in North-West Europe. In (Illing, L. V. and Hobson, G.D; Eds). *Petroleum Geology of the Continental Shelf of North-West Europe*. London, Heyden for Institute of Petroleum, 3-29.

ZIEGLER, P. A., 1982. *Geological Atlas of Western and Central Europe*. (Maps and accompanying memoir:130 pp) Elsevier, Shell International Petroleum Co.

ZIEGLER, P. A., 1988. *Evolution of Arctic – North Atlantic and Western Tethys.* Tulsa, American Association of Petroleum Geologists, 198 pp.

NOTES

NOTES